AMERICA'S FORESTED WETLANDS

FOREST HISTORY SOCIETY ISSUES SERIES

The Forest History Society was founded in 1946. Since that time, the Society, through its research, reference, and publications programs, has advanced forest and conservation history scholarship. At the same time, it has translated that scholarship into formats useful for people with policy and management responsibilities. For seven decades the Society has worked to demonstrate history's significant utility.

The Forest History Society's Issues Series is one of the Society's most explicit contributions to history's utility. The Society selects issues of importance today that also have significant historical dimensions. Then we invite authors of demonstrated knowledge to examine an issue and synthesize its substantial literature, while keeping the general reader in mind.

The final and most important step is making these authoritative overviews available. Toward that end, an initial distribution is made to people with education, management, policy, or legislative responsibilities who will benefit from a deepened understanding of how a particular issue began and evolved. The books are commonly used in education programs throughout North America and beyond.

The Issues Series—like its Forest History Society sponsor—is nonadvocatory and aims to present a balanced rendition of often contentious issues.

Other Issues Series titles available from the Forest History Society:

AMERICA'S FORESTED

Wetlands

From Wasteland to Valued Resource

JEFFREY K. STINE

Forest History Society
Durham, North Carolina

THE FOREST HISTORY SOCIETY

The Forest History Society is a nonprofit educational and research institution dedicated to the advancement of historical understanding of human interaction with the forest environment. It was established in 1946. Interpretations and conclusions in FHS publications are those of the authors; the institution takes responsibility for the selection of topics, competency of the authors, and their freedom of inquiry.

This book was published with support from the Lynn W. Day Endowment for Forest History Publications, the American Forest & Paper Association, International Paper Company and the MeadWestvaco Corporation.

Printed in the United States of America

Forest History Society
701 William Vickers Avenue
Durham, North Carolina 27701
(919) 682-9319
www.foresthistory.org

Library of Congress Cataloging-in-Publication Data

Stine, Jeffrey K.
  America's forested wetlands : from wasteland to valued resource / Jeffrey K. Stine. -- 1st ed.
      p. cm. -- (Forest History Society issues series)
  Includes index.
  Summary: "America's Forested Wetlands chronicles the history of American attitudes and actions toward wetlands. Covering the ecological contributions of wetlands, the history of draining and filling, and the evolution of public policy, the book is an essential primer on one of America's most persistent and contentious issues in natural resource management"--Provided by publisher.
  ISBN-13: 978-0-89030-071-8 (pbk. : alk. paper)
  1. Wetland forestry--United States--History. 2. Wetland ecology--United States--History. 3. Forested wetlands--United States--History. I. Title.
  SD410.9.S75 2008
  333.91'80973--dc22
                                    2008007955

CONTENTS

Since European settlement, the United States has converted just over half of its wetlands to other uses. Wetlands were perceived as wastelands to be harnessed for agricultural productivity or feared because they harbored pestilence or predators. Today, we recognize that wetlands provide essential ecological services, but debates continue over how best to achieve the goal of wise resource management. The history of America's forested wetlands offers valuable insights for future discussion and decision-making:

- European settlers to North America encountered unimaginably vast and varied wetland settings, many of which provided them with needed sources of food, fodder, and building materials. As the nation expanded during the 18th and 19th centuries, swamps and marshes inhibited travel and development, causing them to be viewed as wastelands by the majority of Americans.

- By the 19th century, wetlands were widely filled and drained for agricultural, commercial, and municipal use. The few federal wetlands laws and regulations that were enacted encouraged the transformation, not the preservation, of such landscapes.

- After the Civil War, the South's cypress swamps and extensive bottomland hardwood forests fueled a robust expansion in industrial forestry. Steam-powered pullboats, logging railroads, and ambitious swamp-drainage efforts sustained a decades-long logging boom.

- Mechanization expanded dramatically the pace and economic feasibility of converting wetlands across the nation to other uses during the late 19th century. By far the largest single devourer of wet landscapes was agriculture (87%), but mining, river impoundments, timber production, transportation, and municipal and industrial development also contributed to these losses.

■ The loss of wetlands has tended to occur piecemeal, but it is the cumulative nature of encroachments that has posed the greatest threat to this resource base.

■ By the early 20th century, the United States had recognized that wetlands—like its other natural resources—were not inexhaustible. The decline of egrets and similar nongame birds revealed the importance of setting aside strategic wetland environments as breeding and nesting grounds.

■ The centrality of wetlands as wildlife habitat gained widespread public attention during the 1930s, when the steep declines in waterfowl populations shocked the nation's sport hunters. Congress responded in 1934 by passing the Migratory Bird Hunting Stamp Act to raise funds for wetlands conservation along the country's major flyways.

■ During the mid-20th century, the maturing science of ecology contributed to public understanding of wetlands as an ecosystem and the ecological services they provided, such as water quality and supply, flood and drought modulation, storm protection, and biological diversity.

■ Popular support for wetlands protection increased after World War II because of recognition of the economic consequences of destruction. Once wetlands were lost, their natural functions would have to be replaced by costly water treatment and sewage disposal facilities, flood control structures, and other water resource development projects.

■ Aesthetic appreciation of wetlands also rose, especially during the 1960s and thereafter, as outdoor recreation gained greater popularity and people turned to river swamps as relatively unspoiled retreats.

■ Individual states began regulating the use of wetlands during the 1960s. Federal efforts to curb the loss of wetlands emerged with the passage of the Federal Water Pollution Control Act amendments of 1972 that began regulating the discharge of dredged and fill material into the nation's waters.

- Tensions between property rights and the public good worked to make wetlands regulation a contentious issue in the late 20th century. The Clean Water Act of 1977 provided Section 404 regulatory exemptions for normal farming, forestry, and ranching. Subsequent judicial rulings have continued to refine the jurisdiction and enforcement of this regulation.

- The physically ambiguous characteristics of wetlands—they occupy transitional areas between dry terrain and open water—have contributed to socially ambivalent perceptions and confusion about what wetlands are and how they should be treated. These debates have dominated regulatory discussions.

- Roughly 75 percent of all wetlands in the contiguous United States are privately owned, and they directly or indirectly affect the broader public good through their impact on water quality and supply, the severity of flood and storm damage, and biological diversity. The benefits of protecting and maintaining wetlands have tended to accrue to society at large rather than to individual landowners.

- In the 1990s the federal government launched a policy goal of no net loss of wetlands. Mitigation programs that allowed landowners to create or restore wetlands for natural wetlands that would be filled in have met with varied results.

- In the 20 years from the mid-1950s to the mid-1970s, more than 9 million acres of wetlands disappeared in the contiguous United States, an average loss of 458,000 acres per year. The annual loss rate fell to about 290,000 acres between the mid-1970s and mid-1980s, when the nation's wetlands total declined by some 2.6 million acres. Today, forested wetlands cover about 52 million acres in the contiguous 48 states and another 13 million in Alaska. Although 65 percent of this area is located in the Southeast, forested wetlands are found throughout the country.

- In the early 21st century wetland conservation continues to be an issue of consistent concern marked by peaks of policy attention. It is likely that society will continue to grapple with this issue as the importance of wetlands will only increase in the future. Government involvement will need to be balanced with market-oriented and voluntary efforts in an ever-vigilant manner.

Wetlands have long evoked conflicting attitudes. As transitional areas between dry terrain and open water, occupying the border between solidity and liquidity, they are one of nature's most biologically productive environments. Yet they also impede travel, encumber development, and harbor dangers both real and imaged. Over time, these physically ambiguous landscapes have engendered socially ambivalent perceptions about what they represent and how they should be treated.

At the time of European settlement, wetlands covered roughly 11 percent of the territory that eventually became the contiguous United States. By the dawn of the 21st century, this 221-million-acre wetlands inheritance had been reduced to just over 105 million acres. Prior to the 1930s, few people worried about the cumulative loss of these landscapes. In fact, their conversion to dry (and more "usable") land was generally applauded. Indifference and dislike typified the dominant American attitudes toward wetlands.

The coining of the generic term "wetlands" during the mid-20th century was an attempt to counter a broad range of negative ideas about a complex type of natural environment. The very diversity of names that had been applied to wet habitats (see Figure 1) reflected the broad-scale differences in their locations, characteristics, and cultural associations. While each of the names—from swamps to bogs, mudflats to vernal pools—emphasized different aspects, the environments themselves share common characteristics: they are all permanently or intermittently saturated or inundated with water, and they all support vegetation adapted to saturated or poorly aerated soil.

Figure 1. Some of the Names Given to Wetlands.

Swamps, marshes, bogs, mires, quagmires, sloughs, bayous, lagoons, estuaries, fens, flats, meadows, moors, meres, morasses, mud holes, mud banks, bays, brakes, canebrakes, cypress brakes, wallows, hollows, swales, sumps, seeps, tules, floodplains, battures, bottoms, first bottoms, riverbottoms, bottomlands, blackwater bottomlands, peatlands, fenlands, tidelands, lowlands, muck lands, haylands, meadowlands, moorlands, overflowed lands, drowned lands, batture lands, marshlands, salt marsh lands, swamplands, tidal swamps, coastal swamps, marine swamps, saltwater swamps, muck swamps, brownwater swamps, peat swamps, bay swamps, back swamps, tule swamps, reed swamps, cane swamps, shrub swamps, thicket swamps, swamp woods, cypress swamps, tamarack swamps, tupelo swamps, mangrove swamps, mangrove forests, swamp forests, bottomland hardwood forests, drunken forests, trembling prairies, flotants, floating fens, floating bogs, quaking bogs, blanket bogs, shrub bogs, forested bogs, peat bogs, kettle-hole bogs, cranberry bogs, hammocks, cypress domes, cypress bays, bayheads, mangles, glades, everglades, gator holes, hog wallows, buffalo wallows, oxbows, savannas, salinas, pantanos, polders, backwaters, water meadows, bog meadows, beaver meadows, sedge meadows, sedge marshes, tule marshes, cattail marshes, cow marshes, glacial marshes, muck marshes, tidal marshes, tidewater marshes, salt marshes, salt meadows, salt flats, sandflats, mudflats, tidal flats, coastal flats, pine flats, pitcher plant flats, wet flats, wet forests, wet meadows, wet lands, wet bogs, wet prairies, wet savannas, wet tundra, taigas, muskegs, Carolina bays, Delmarva bays, Delmarva potholes, pocosins, loblollies, carrs, shrub-carrs, fen-carrs, calcareous fens, mountain fens, flatwoods, pine flatwoods, pine barrens, quicksand, ciénegas, playas, playa lakes, vernal pools, prairie potholes.

Today, wetlands are recognized for their broad range of ecological services. They improve water quality by physically and chemically trapping nutrients, sediments, and pollution loads. They regulate water flow by modulating floods and droughts. They defend shorelines from erosive wave action and storm tides. They also contribute to water supply—some recharge aquifers through the promotion of groundwater infiltration, others feed lakes and streams through the gradual release of absorbed water. Their sequestration of carbon helps lower the level of greenhouse gas in the atmosphere. Peatlands, in particular, act as a natural sink for the airborne pollutant mercury. By providing food, shelter, and breeding grounds, wetlands serve as essential habitats for hundreds of species of fish, shellfish, waterfowl, and wildlife, many of which are commercially important. They sustain about a third of the species currently considered threatened or endangered in the United States, and the uniqueness of some wetlands makes them prime reservoirs of genetic diversity. Their harvestable resources—such as timber, game animals, peat, wild rice, berries, hay, and grasses—have long been valued by society. And their recreational, educational, and aesthetic benefits—which present opportunities for bird watching, hiking, canoeing, picnicking, hunting, fishing, photography, ecotourism, environmental education, and research—have accelerated in popularity since the 1960s.

This booklet explores the evolution of American attitudes and actions toward wetlands in general and toward forested wetlands in particular, explaining why these landscapes have posed such challenges to citizens and policy makers and why they are likely to remain a perennial political concern. History cannot enable us to predict the precise choices that will confront American society in the years to come, but it can assist us in understanding the origins and implications of competing visions for this invaluable but threatened natural resource.

CHAPTER ONE

Nation Building

The first European settlers in North America encountered an extraordinarily rich array of wetland environments, which Native American peoples had, for centuries, relied upon for food, shelter, transportation, and protection. The colonists initially shunned swamps and marshes in favor of uplands for siting their buildings, roads, pastures, and farm fields, but soon the new immigrants recognized that their prosperity—and sometimes their survival—would hinge on these water-soaked landscapes, with their bounty of berries, fish, and fowl, as well as fodder

Coastal marshes, like the one depicted in Thomas Moran's etching *Passaic Meadows* (c. 1873), provided early European settlers with important natural resources. Courtesy Graphic Arts Collection, National Museum of American History, Smithsonian Institution.

for domesticated animals, reeds for thatching, trees for fuel and timber, and game animals for skins and meat. During the 18th century, expansions in commerce, farm production, and population centers lessened the coastal settlements' dependency on nearby tidal marshes and riparian meadows for food, fuel, and building materials. Wetlands became increasingly valued as sites to be reclaimed for agriculture and other land development.

Fur traders were among the earliest Euramericans to explore the continent's interior, where they were drawn to the seemingly limitless web of streams and wetlands teeming with muskrat, otter, mink, and beaver. Although inland swamp forests supplied riches to trappers, the pioneers who followed them sought a different kind of fortune. To them, the extensive forested wetlands posed formidable barriers to travel and homesteading—too fluid to build a road upon, yet not suitable for boat traffic, either. Because such landscapes had been eliminated long ago in England and other parts of Europe, they were viewed apprehensively as strange, disagreeable places. Unfamiliarity combined with superstition and fear kept many Euramericans from even venturing into swamplands, which they considered foreboding and inherently dangerous. Wetlands soon came to be stigmatized as wastelands, as areas of little value unless drained or filled for agricultural, commercial, or municipal use. Nevertheless, the abundance of undeveloped dry lands and the time and expense required to dewater wetlands meant that the majority of inland swamps were bypassed during the initial European settlement of North America. Whole pockets of land in the South and Midwest remained untouched, eschewed by farmers and land speculators who were able to clear uplands of forests in half the time required to drain and clear an equivalent expanse of swampland.

As the nation became increasingly populated, however, developers looked anew at the largely unoccupied wetlands, especially those close to existing towns, villages, and farms. Some of the earliest systematic conversions of wetlands in America took place during the 17th and 18th centuries along the east coast. With hay in high demand for horses, farmers diked and drained salt and freshwater marshes to create fields capable of producing multiple annual crops of fodder. This small-scale activity continued during the early 19th century in New England, where property owners dug narrow drainage ditches by hand to turn small marshes and meadows into farmland. By midcentury, mechanization had expanded

Transportation through forested wetlands like the Great Dismal Swamp was difficult even under the best circumstances. Photo by C. E. Russell for the U.S. Forest Service, Forest History Society Photo Collection.

the scale and reduced the per acre costs of dewatering wetlands. Later in the century, entrepreneurs in California and the South incorporated elaborate networks of levees, pumps, and drainage canals into their highly ambitious engineering schemes.

One thing that did not change during this period of nation building was the perception that soggy terrain posed a public health hazard. Until the late 19th century, the widely held miasmic theory linked illness with exposure to vapors emanating from marshes rife with rotting vegetation. Although the germ theory of disease gradually undercut medical concerns about the poisoned air, or miasmas, once thought to be associated with dank, humid lowlands, the wetlands themselves remained under a cloud of suspicion. Concern about the menace of insect-breeding swamps—especially after the turn of the 20th century, when mosquitoes became recognized as a disease vector for malaria and other waterborne illnesses—reinforced the view that

Alaska contains the nation's largest concentration of wetlands, much of it wet tundra, which serves as critically important habitat for migratory birds and wildlife. This aerial photograph shows the Yukon Delta National Wildlife Refuge. Photo by Nancy Marx, courtesy U.S. Fish and Wildlife Service.

wetlands bred pestilence. Indeed, malaria (a word derived in the mid-18th century from the Italian phrase *mala aria*, meaning "bad air") was still commonly called "swamp fever." This attitude made it easy for cities such as Boston, New York, and Washington to dump the voluminous solid wastes they generated into their urban marshlands and thereby create new (and highly prized) building sites.

The few federal wetlands laws and regulations enacted during the 19th century sought to transform, not preserve, such landscapes. The Swamp Land Act of 1849 is a case in point. Its goal was to promote economic growth by encouraging development of heretofore sparsely settled lands. It granted to the state of Louisiana all unsold federal "swamp and over-flowed lands" deemed unfit for cultivation, pending the state's assurance that it would use the revenue from the sale of these lands to drain them and protect them from flooding by building levees. The following year,

Congress extended the Swamp Land Act provisions to 12 other states (Alabama, Arkansas, California, Florida, Illinois, Indiana, Iowa, Michigan, Mississippi, Missouri, Ohio, and Wisconsin) containing large blocks of federally owned wetlands, and in 1860, it added Minnesota and Oregon. Through this legislation, the federal government ultimately ceded nearly 65 million acres of flood-prone land to the states. Florida received the largest grant, at more than 20 million acres. Louisiana was second, at nearly 9.4 million acres, followed by Arkansas at about 7.7 million and Michigan at over 5.6 million. Mississippi, Missouri, and Wisconsin each gained title to more than 3 million acres and California received over 2 million.

One by one, the states passed their own drainage laws, which typically established local drainage districts empowered to construct and maintain the ditches and canals used to carry away excess water from individual farms. The late-19th-century drainage booms were especially significant in the Midwest, where landowners installed rows of mass-produced, perforated clay pipes—known as drainage tiles—beneath their fields to capture and remove the near-surface water from hundreds of thousands of acres of seasonally saturated prairies in states like Ohio, Indiana, Illinois,

Practitioners of the emerging field of agricultural engineering devoted much of their efforts to draining lands for crop production. John H. Klippart, the corresponding secretary of the Ohio State Board of Agriculture, predicted in the third edition of his popular textbook, *The Principles and Practice of Land Drainage* (1888), that:

"Drainage will soon become a new field of industry, which will demand more engineers than the railways have done—more 'surveyors' than the western wilderness. It is a field in which thousands and tens of thousands will find employment, and will go on increasing until the greater portion of the whole North American continent will be underdrained."

Iowa, and Minnesota. Thousands upon thousands of additional acres of wet forests in the lowlands bordering the Great Lakes were also lost to this great wave of engineered land drainage. Eventually, about 45 million acres was transformed in this fashion, including 29 percent of the surface area of Indiana, 27 percent of Illinois, 22 percent of Iowa, and 19 percent of Ohio. Boosted by land sales, mechanization, and sympathetic legislative and legal developments, drainage districts flourished during the first two decades of the 20th century, when the acreage under their combined jurisdictions exceeded in size the state of Missouri. The federal government helped sustain the rapid pace of wetlands conversion through a series of drainage projects that were encouraged, built, subsidized, or wholly financed by the U.S. Department of Agriculture's Soil Conservation Service or the U.S. Army Corps of Engineers.

Agricultural expansion may have prompted the lion's share of drainage schemes, but public health concerns also played a role. Scientific understanding of how to address the spread of malaria fueled an extensive mosquito-reduction campaign. New Jersey state entomologist John B. Smith orchestrated one of the most aggressive of these early efforts in 1900. He embarked on a broad-scale mosquito control effort, incorporating platoons of motorized ditch-diggers to cut drainage channels in thousands of acres of the state's coastal marshes. Smith then supplemented this dewatering effort with dredging machines mounted on barges, which pumped sand from river bottoms to fill in lowlands.

The mosquito-control campaign proved successful, driving down the mosquito populations along beaches and in low-lying areas adjacent to cities, and driving up the value of property near the projects. Gradually, other mosquito-plagued villages and towns undertook similar efforts and the approach gained further credibility thanks to the success of similar eradication projects in the Panama Canal construction zone.

During the 1930s, the mosquito-control programs of two New Deal agencies—the Works Progress Administration and the Civilian Conservation Corps—dewatered large expanses of New England's remaining salt marshes and contributed to significant reduction of swampland in Florida and other parts of the country. Local government officials tended to look favorably upon federal drainage projects within their jurisdictions, because such initiatives brought with them infusions of construction funds and promises of increased tax revenue from the reclaimed land. Ironically, the use of

DDT in mosquito control eventually lessened the public-health pressures to destroy wetlands, as the application of insecticides, together with the widespread installation of window and door screens, effectively stemmed the spread of malaria.

The unprecedented levels of immigration to the United States during the late 19th century and early 20th century placed a tremendous burden on

In his 1901 textbook, *Mosquitoes: How They Live; How They Carry Disease; How They Are Classified; How They May Be Destroyed*, L.O. Howard of the U.S. Department of Agriculture summed up the state of knowledge about mosquitoes and their relationship to human disease. His negative views of wetlands reflected the thinking of many at the time. According to Howard:

"It is difficult in any case, and entirely without reference to the question of mosquito-supply, to see why swamp-land should be allowed to exist. There are many large tracts of swamp-land which could be drained with a comparatively slight expenditure of money, and which, when once reclaimed, would be of very great value for agricultural purposes. There is a great deal of this land in the immediate vicinity of many large communities which suffer from the attacks of mosquitoes and which are more or less malarious. In such instances, community drainage-work should be undertaken for the health and comfort of the community. Misguided owners of swamp-land, if they cannot be made to see that such measures would bring dollars and cents into their pockets, should be coerced."

the nation's major cities. In an effort to disperse people around the country, expand the national economy, and ensure an adequate food supply, the federal government strove to open more lands to farming. Toward this end,

Summarizing the ongoing congressional debates over the appropriate federal role in advancing the conversion of the nation's wetlands, the magazine *The American Contractor* reported in 1907:

"The national government seems on the eve of undertaking the reclamation of the sixty million acres of swamp lands lying scattered from coast to coast and from Canada to the Gulf, so distributed that all regions may be benefited and so rich in productive possibilities that if the work is accomplished the wealth producing resources of the country will be materially increased. If in the end the government is successful in bringing this area under cultivation it will provide a million and a half families with forty-acre farms and make possible a healthful, rural productive life for some eight million persons. These lands would make homes and heritages for the poor, the unfortunate, the unattached, be they native or foreign, in all the cities of the United States. Where these lands now have little value they might be brought to such productiveness as to yield many millions annually in revenues to the country, for in richness the soil is without a rival."

Congress directed the Department of Agriculture in 1906 to conduct the nation's first comprehensive inventory of freshwater wetlands. More specifically, the department was asked to identify all of the swamp and overflowed lands east of the 115th meridian (near the eastern border of Nevada) that could be filled and drained for cultivation. According to the inventory— which excluded eastern tidal marshes, along with the entire far West—an estimated 79 million acres could be profitably converted to cropland.

The Department of Agriculture undertook a second national wetlands inventory in 1922, this time surveying all 48 states. The department's Bureau of Land Economics concluded that an area totaling approximately 113,537,000 acres was "too wet for cultivation," of which about 91,543,000 acres would be "suitable for agriculture after reclamation." From an economic standpoint, however, bureau officials reported that only 75 million acres warranted drainage, since the other marsh, swamp, and timbered overflow lands were either more valuable left alone for "fish, wild fowl, furbearing animals, recreational purposes, or for water conservation" or were so heavily forested that the combined costs of drainage and land clearing would far exceed the value of the reclaimed farm fields.

In 1940, the Soil Conservation Service completed a drainage reconnaissance survey in which it calculated the nation's wetland reserves at 97,332,000 acres. Thirteen years later, the Department of Agriculture issued a report placing the total acreage of wetlands at 125 million, with an estimated 50 million of those acres suitable for tillage or pastureland if drained. Unfortunately for policy makers, these early inventories were not directly comparable with one another because of the significant differences in the territories they evaluated, the survey methods they employed, and the physical and biological criteria they used for defining wetlands. As a result, decision making proceeded piecemeal, with emphasis on multiple individual projects. During the 1940s and 1950s, the Department of Agriculture's Agricultural Conservation Program subsidized thousands of small drainage works to reclaim wetlands for cultivation, while the department's Soil Conservation Service simultaneously promoted construction of small impoundments that inadvertently consumed numerous isolated wetlands. Between 1940 and 1977, the Agricultural Conservation Program alone assisted in the drainage of about 57 million acres. These efforts were reinforced by the Federal Watershed Protection and Flood Prevention Act of 1953, which directed the Army Corps of Engineers and Department of

Red mangroves, such as these in the Florida Everglades, help protect shorelines from wave and storm damage and provide prime breeding grounds
for fish and shellfish. Photo by Ann Vileisis.

Agriculture to coordinate their flood control and agricultural drainage
projects by working together with state and local governments in the construction and maintenance of drainage outlet channels in major rivers and
their upstream tributaries.

　　To the extent that wetlands constituted a public policy concern prior
to the 1960s, they were set largely within a framework of elimination. The
federal government's role was to facilitate conversion to dry lands that
could be farmed or otherwise developed. Federal programs to remake the
landscapes of the eastern two-thirds of the nation by draining wetlands—
such as the ambitious flood control projects of the Army Corps of Engineers
and Tennessee Valley Authority, and the small-scale reclamation projects
of the Soil Conservation Service and Agricultural Conservation Program—
were, in a very real sense, the flip side of the government's grand irrigation
schemes for the western states. The infrastructural exoskeletons of the
massive water storage and distribution systems built to irrigate the West's

arid and semiarid lands were visually arresting, yet their impact on the environment was essentially on par with the elaborate, widespread, but less conspicuous efforts to dewater wetlands and create new agricultural lands east of the 100th meridian. Ironically, many western irrigation systems necessitated the construction of complementary drainage projects to minimize the long-term threats of waterlogging and salinization of soils in irrigated fields. Moreover, by diverting water from natural streams and rivers, irrigation projects caused significant damage to riparian wetlands, especially in places like central California, where the reclamation of delta lands—those so-called overflowed lands subject to periodic flooding—involved diking and draining marshes to create cropland.

The greatest single devourer of wetlands has been the spread of agriculture, much of it enabled since the mid-19th century by government programs, including federal land transfers, farm subsidies, tax deductions and credits, and federal and state reclamation projects. Nearly 80 percent of the wetlands lost in the United States since World War II were filled and drained to create farmland. The other factors contributing to the reduction of wet landscapes included municipal and suburban growth, road and railroad building, water supply, flood control, recreational facilities, navigational improvements, forestry activities, and oil, gas, and mineral extraction. Increasing levels of air and water pollution have also taken their toll on marshes, bogs, and swamps. The piecemeal and cumulative nature of these varied encroachments on wetlands has made this a particularly difficult problem to address. For decades, individual insults to wetland environments were often insignificant in and of themselves. When added together, however, their impact has inflicted substantial harm.

CHAPTER TWO

Wet Forests

North America's forested wetlands come in many shapes, sizes, and locations. Differences in their water regimes, soils, and vegetation produce a broad spectrum of characteristics. Their common distinguishing feature—aside from soils that are periodically flooded or saturated—is the presence of water-tolerant trees, which may be broad-leaved (such as alder, ash, bay, or gum) or narrow-leaved (such as spruce, cedar, cypress, or tamarack), deciduous or evergreen. A wetland is considered forested if at least 30 percent of its expanse is covered by trees 20 feet high or taller. Today, wet forests occupy approximately 52 million acres in the contiguous 48 states and about 13 million acres in Alaska. The largest concentrations are in the Southeast, which contains about 65 percent of the nation's forested wetlands. Because southern wooded swamps and bottomland hardwood forests tend to be highly productive, many of them have become important sites of commercial timber operations.

Wet forests may be found in a variety of places, such as around ponds and lakes, along slow-moving streams, or within alluvial floodplains, shallow oxbow lakes, isolated depressions, areas with high groundwater tables, poorly drained lowlands, and swamps. Many forested wetlands are subject to seasonal or periodic flooding, which means that standing water in these woodlands is intermittent. Floodwaters may cover bottomland hardwoods, for instance, anywhere from three to 20 weeks per year. Forested wetlands in different areas of the country have different prominent tree species (see Figure 2). Loblolly pine forests, for example, form a specialized type of wooded wetland in the southeastern coastal plains. Loblolly is an old English word meaning a thick gruel, or a mire or mud hole, and indeed, loblolly pines are often engulfed by shallow, cold-weather ponds.

Figure 2. Typical Tree Species in U.S. Forested Wetlands.

Northeast: northern white cedar, red maple, tamarack, black ash, green ash, balsam fir, black spruce, yellow birch, and American elm

Mid-Atlantic: red maple, silver maple, black gum, sweet bay, red bay, willow oak, swamp chestnut oak, pin oak, green ash, pitch pine, loblolly pine, pond pine, sweet gum, and green gum

South: Atlantic white cedar, bald cypress, pond cypress, black gum, sweet gum, red gum, green ash, American elm, sycamore, longleaf pine, loblolly pine, slash pine, pond pine, water oak, swamp laurel oak, cherrybark oak, swamp tupelo, water tupelo, and black willow

West: sweet gum, willow oak, water oak, overcup oak, water hickory, sugarberry, cottonwood, quaking aspen, box elder, alders, willows, and elms

Northwest: red alder, western hemlock, western red cedar, Oregon ash, cottonwood, and willows

Alaska: black spruce, tamarack, lodgepole pine, balsam fir, mountain and western hemlock, Sitka spruce, and red alder

In fact, most wetland loblolly sites show signs of standing water only during the nongrowth season of winter, with their soils remaining saturated through the early spring. The surface of loblolly forests can therefore appear dry for most of the year. Other specialized types of forested wetlands include pine barrens in the Mid-Atlantic and northern portions of Michigan, Wisconsin, and Minnesota; pocosins (an Algonquin Indian word meaning "swamp on a hill"), which are wooded bogs occurring within the flat divides that traverse the southern Atlantic coastal plain; and mangrove forests around the tip of Florida.

Where water was not too deep, horses and oxen could be used to haul logs out of forested wetlands. Photo by Sidney V. Streator, Forest History Society Photo Collection.

The type, breadth, and location of a forested wetland determined the ease with which its trees could be harvested, and consequently influenced when such woodlands were first logged. Eighteenth- and 19th-century lumbermen found many of the continent's larger and wetter swamp forests virtually impenetrable. Without rivers or large streams for rafting, or dry land capable of supporting roadways, the expense of transporting logs often outstripped the lumber's market value. There were exceptions, of course. The northern wet forests in Michigan, for example, proved relatively easy to log during the region's long, cold winters, when the snow-covered, frozen earth made access easy for lumberjacks and their equipment. The need for roads, railroads, and canals was minimal. Draft animals could efficiently skid felled trees across the ice and snow to riverbanks, where the logs would be stockpiled until spring thaws allowed them to be driven down the flood-swollen currents to sawmills.

George Washington and other 18th-century land speculators believed that southern Virginia's Great Dismal Swamp could be drained and profitably farmed. This early hand-dug drainage canal was widely known as "Washington's Ditch," in honor of the president and his early surveys of the area. Photo by Ann Vileisis.

The South's extensive swamplands did not offer timbermen the seasonal climatic advantages enjoyed by their northern counterparts. Logging in these warmer latitudes required a different approach. Longleaf pine in the region's more readily accessible wetlands had been widely harvested for naval stores in the 18th century; then farmers used fire to clear some of these upland bogs—or pocosins—for the cultivation of crops. In the Carolinas, property owners had ditches dug by hand to dewater their Piedmont swamps, although such land conversions were limited prior to the mid-19th-century introduction of steam-powered dredges. Mechanically excavated drainage canals had the added benefit of providing a watercourse for floating logs out of the larger wet forests, increasing yields and profits.

This 1928 photograph of cypresses in Louisiana's Bayou Queue de Tortue illustrates the swollen butts and knees that anchor the trees in swampy conditions. Photo by G. H. Lantz for the U.S. Forest Service, Forest History Society Photo Collection.

Cypress swamps represented the South's most dramatic and best-known type of forested wetland. By the 18th century, cypress lumber had become highly prized for its exceptional durability (it resists both insect damage and decay, even when exposed to water), its ease of being worked with hand tools (it is a straight-grained, soft wood whose boards do not warp when used green), and its low flammability (it contains little resin). Because cypress grew in the warm, shallow waters of southern lakes, swamps, and streams, harvesting the dense, heavy trees proved unusually difficult. The use of horses or oxen was rarely an option. Alternative methods of felling and transporting the trees had to be developed. Depending upon the local conditions and time of year, loggers often could not even plant their feet on firm ground to swing their axes. French woodsmen in Louisiana actually learned to cut cypress trees while standing in small boats or balancing

Felling trees in deepwater swamps required innovative techniques.
Forest History Society Photo Collection.

themselves on narrow scaffolds that they had wedged into the trees' broad
buttresses. Once downed, green cypress trees sank, making it difficult to
chop off the submerged limbs. Moreover, because the logs could not be
floated, they had to be wrestled onto rafts made from other wood and then
towed.

By the mid-18th century, however, timber workers had solved the buoy-
ancy problem. They girdled the cypress trees anywhere from a few months
to two years ahead of felling. The sap-drained, deadened trees became suf-
ficiently dry to float, which facilitated trimming branches from the logs and
lashing them together for transport. As the scale of the cypress industry
expanded, lumberjacks in the Mississippi River delta would fell trees, saw
them into 10- to 12-foot lengths, and leave them in place until the next
flood, when the logs would be corralled and driven to downstream mills.

Investments in cypress logging surged during the late 19th century as
timber companies from the Great Lakes states began relocating their
operations to the Deep South. With this increased capital came increased

The Bowie Lumber Company operated this quarterboat and dredge in Louisiana during the early 20th century. To gain access to cypress swamps, southern lumber companies built canals that enabled them to harvest trees via pullboats. Forest History Society Photo Collection.

mechanization. Steam-powered skidders introduced in the 1880s revolutionized the ability to winch bald and pond cypress logs to a central location and helped bring to an end the seasonal rhythms of harvesting these wooded swamps. By the 1890s, when steam-powered skidders were commonly mounted on large, flat-bottom scows—known as pullboats—industrial cypress logging became economically feasible. This new method usually required dredge boats to excavate strategically plotted canals, upon which pullboats could then be towed to successive logging sites. The powerful steam engines on these vessels turned large drums to wind in long, heavy cables, in much the same manner an angler would crank the reel on a fishing rod. After anchoring the pullboats firmly to tree stumps or pilings, work crews hauled the slack cable up to 3,000 feet into the swamp and attached it to as many as 20 felled trees. The engines

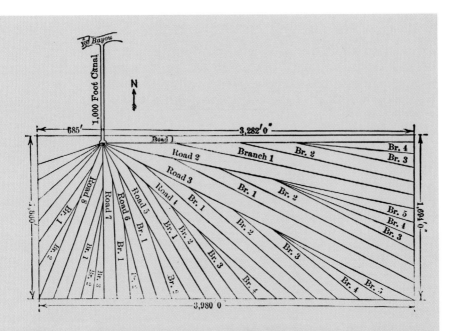

Figure 3. Pullboat operators created a fanlike pattern across swamp forests as they winched in the felled trees to a central location. This 1923 diagram shows the layout of pullboat skid runs in Louisiana. Forest History Society Collection.

would then spool the cable onto the drum, thereby dragging the logs to the canal (see Figure 3). The process was repeated as many times as necessary before the pullboat advanced to its next mooring. The assembled logs were later formed into rafts and towed to processing plants.

During the next phase of technological innovation in cypress logging, the construction of narrow-gauge railroads allowed lumbermen to surpass the reach of pullboats and economize on the transport of timber to mills and markets. Early railroad spur lines that crossed forested wetlands were often underlaid with continuous beds of small tree trunks, akin to the corduroy roads constructed on other saturated landscapes. In many locations, cypress logs were delivered to the railroad lines via overhead carriages that rode along cableways rigged to the tops of tall trees and extending as much as 600 feet into the swamp. After an area was harvested, the overhead skidding equipment was moved down the rail line about a thousand feet,

Logging railroads greatly expanded the scale of commercial lumber operations in wet forests during the late 19th century. Photo by Burgert Brothers, Forest History Society Photo Collection.

where the entire system would be reassembled. The combination of steam-powered pullboats, logging railroads, cableway skidders, and an expanded swamp drainage effort—together with an aggressive international sales campaign by cypress dealers—helped ignite a logging boom that lasted from 1890 to 1925. In 1899, for example, southern mills turned out some

The high-water marks on these trees in Louisiana's Atchafalaya swamp
attest to the periodic flooding characteristic of this type of wetland.
Photo by Ann Vileisis.

Bottomland hardwood forests suffered substantial losses during the 20th century, often because of conversions to farmland. This sugar field in Bayou La Fourche, Louisiana, is surrounded by forested wetlands. Photo by Ann Vileisis.

495 million board feet of cypress lumber. By 1913, their output exceeded 1 billion board feet. The boom collapsed in the mid-1920s, when most of the old-growth cypress stands had been exhausted.

The bottomland hardwoods found along the river valley floodplains of Louisiana, Arkansas, Mississippi, Alabama, Florida, Georgia, the Carolinas, and Virginia constituted another commercially important type of southern forested wetland. The Mississippi River valley's wet woodlands were unmatched in their geographic scope; in pre-Columbian times, they occupied more than 26 million acres, stretching some 600 miles from south-central Louisiana to southern Illinois, with interconnected lowland forests fanning out from the Mississippi's major tributaries. (By the late 1930s, this vast forested wetland had been reduced to less than 12 million acres; by the 1990s, only about 5 million acres remained.) The timberlands enveloping the lower reaches of the South's other river systems

New technologies helped open America's larger swamps to commercial forestry. This Caterpillar tractor was hauling logs out of a forested wetland in Georgia in 1929. Forest History Society Photo Collection.

formed fertile, free-standing corridors shaded by water-tolerant trees capable of withstanding the scouring and sediment deposits that accompany seasonal flooding.

As with cypress logging, wetland conditions constrained the early harvesting of bottomland hardwood forests. Logging rarely extended much beyond the banks of the streams and rivers that flowed through them. It was not uncommon, therefore, for the interiors of the South's larger swamp forests to escape development, allowing these important biological preserves to survive intact. In the 1920s, however, motorized draglines and bulldozers made draining and clearing these once imposing landscapes far more economical. This technological capability opened whole new areas of the South's bottomland forests to commercial logging. Many of these woodlands, especially in the Mississippi River delta, were later converted to farmland. Although floodplain hardwoods in the Carolinas, Georgia, and northern Florida suffered less from agricultural expansion, they were more susceptible to being transformed into managed tree farms, such as along Georgia's Ocmulgee and Oconee rivers, where wet forests at higher elevations were logged and the land then prepared for cultivation of pine or other fast-growing species.

Systematic drainage of pine forests along the Atlantic and Gulf coasts did not begin in earnest, however, until after World War II. Initially, some lumber and pulp companies dewatered their forested wetlands to improve access to timber during harvest. Such efforts significantly shortened rain-related logging delays and allowed the use of standard harvesting equipment rather than the more expensive, specialized machinery needed to work in mucky conditions. By the 1950s, forest managers began installing drainage works to aid the restocking and growth of commercially desirable species of pine. This silvicultural practice was patterned on the experience of foresters in Finland, who had significantly increased the timber output in their wet forests through seasonal drainage. By 1960, the rationale for water management in forested wetlands went beyond improving access and increasing tree growth to include fire protection, enhanced regeneration of pine seedlings, protection of soil during management activities, and reduction of soil compaction and puddling.

CHAPTER THREE

Awareness Begins

Until the late 19th century, America's natural resources (wetlands included) were widely believed to be inexhaustible. The fierce and largely unfettered pace of industrial development helped undermine that overly optimistic viewpoint. By the early 20th century, a select handful of wet landscapes had been preserved as breeding and nesting grounds for egrets and similarly threatened nongame birds, but the nascent conservation movement had focused most of its attention on

Numerous bird species, such as these wood storks in Georgia's Harris Neck National Wildlife Refuge, depend upon wetland habitats. Photo by John and Karen Hollingsworth, courtesy U.S. Fish and Wildlife Service.

protecting forests and scenic alpine and coastal settings rather than swamps, bogs, and marshes. Pejorative attitudes toward wetlands were so prevalent in the years preceding World War I that it was not uncommon to find prominent conservationists endorsing drainage efforts. That was soon to change.

Biologists and wildlife managers had been growing increasingly concerned about the wholesale, unchecked elimination of wetlands when, in the early 1930s, precipitous drops in waterfowl populations shocked the voluminous ranks of sport hunters. Attributing the decline to cumulative losses of wetlands in breeding grounds and along flyways, game managers, sportsmen, and organizations like the Izaak Walton League of America and the National Wildlife Federation lobbied for reform. The Migratory Bird Hunting Stamp Act, which Congress enacted in 1934, raised funds for wetlands conservation from hunters over the age of 16 (who were required to purchase the annual federal duck stamps, in addition to state-issued

The U.S. Migratory Bird Hunting Stamp program was launched in 1934 to provide a continuing source of funds for the purchase and protection of wetlands and wildlife habitat. Conservation advocate and Pulitzer Prize-winning cartoonist Jay N. "Ding" Darling designed the first duck stamp, pictured here. Photograph by Jim O'Donnell, courtesy National Postal Museum, Smithsonian Institution.

The renowned wildlife artist, Bob Hines, who had illustrated Rachel Carson's 1955 book, *The Edge of the Sea*, produced this poster for the U.S. Fish and Wildlife Service in 1975. Courtesy National Conservation Training Center Archives/Museum, U.S. Fish and Wildlife Service.

UPPER SOURIS MIGRATORY
WATERFOWL PROJECT AND
MINOT FLOOD CONTROL

Jay N. "Ding" Darling was a popular syndicated newspaper cartoonist and an avid, lifelong conservationist who served briefly (1934–1935) as chief of the Department of Agriculture's Bureau of Biological Survey. His drawings helped increase public appreciation of wetlands. Courtesy National Conservation Training Center Archives/Museum, U.S. Fish and Wildlife Service.

hunting licenses) for the protection of prime waterfowl habitat. The wetland reserves were eventually added to the National Wildlife Refuge System, a program initially administered by the Department of Agriculture's Bureau of Biological Survey.

Guided by their mandate to protect and manage the nation's wildlife resources, Bureau of Biological Survey officials had a long-standing interest in preserving wetland habitat, especially along North America's major flyways. By the 1930s, they had used the 1916 Migratory Bird Treaty between the United States and Canada, together with the Migratory Bird Conservation Act of 1929, to solidify oversight responsibility for a small but strategic patchwork of federally owned wetland refuges. A

In the early 20th century, the extensive bottomland hardwood forests of the Mississippi River delta included broad stands of red gum, like these in southeastern Missouri. Photo by Sidney V. Streator, Forest History Society Photo Collection.

governmental reorganization approved by President Franklin D. Roosevelt in 1939 transferred the Bureau of Biological Survey to the Department of Interior. One year later, the Bureau of Biological Survey merged with the Bureau of Fisheries to form the U.S. Fish and Wildlife Service (FWS). Throughout the decades that followed, this agency's programs and activities drew from the insights of the maturing science of ecology, which was revealing the vital role that wetlands played in the life cycle of aquatic birds and other life forms. By the dawn of the 21st century, the National Wildlife Refuge System of FWS protected wetland and upland habitat in some 442 sites across the country, totaling 91 million acres (76 million of these in Alaska).

Because the Department of Agriculture had restricted its wetlands inventories to potentially farmable terrain, early FWS professionals found themselves handicapped by the lack of a reliable, comprehensive database covering the entirety of the country's wet landscapes and their varying value as wildlife habitat. The Department of Interior addressed this need in the early 1950s by launching its own nationwide inventory under the direction of the Fish and Wildlife Service. To help identify the location and extent of wetlands and determine their contributions to fish, waterfowl, and wildlife populations generally, FWS worked closely with state fish and game agencies. The agency's findings, along with its subsequent tracking of wetlands losses over time, contributed mightily to raising public awareness, informing federal policy, and encouraging private conservation efforts.

The inaugural FWS inventory, *Wetlands of the United States: Their Extent and Their Value to Waterfowl and Other Wildlife*, by Samuel P. Shaw and C. Gordon Fredine (1956), introduced the term *wetlands* into the federal government's official vocabulary. After detailing the status and ecological contributions of these special landscapes, Shaw and Fredine stridently condemned their wanton destruction. "Never before in the Nation's history," they argued, "has it been so necessary to plan for the setting aside of land and water areas to serve the future needs of fish and wildlife, as well as to provide for the recreational needs of people who depend on these resources." Subsequent FWS reports tracked the changing state of wetlands and encouraged research on these imperiled ecosystems. The agency's investigations rarely made the evening news, but as scientific studies steadily documented the multiple ecological functions of wetlands, the resulting knowledge and insights gradually infused discussions of wet environments in other communication venues—from museum and nature center exhibitions to school textbooks, popular magazines, and television documentaries—and helped shape public perceptions and policy. In a pattern common to other conservation campaigns, the heightened appreciation of wetlands did not emerge until the resource itself had suffered serious declines. The political clout and staying power of the post-1950s environmental movement deepened the sympathy among Americans toward the plight of the country's swamps and marshes. The shift in public opinion—which soon placed wetlands protection among the most prominent environmental causes of the late 20th century—was so dramatic that few could have anticipated it only a generation earlier.

The destruction of wetlands had been spurred by perceptions of economic benefit: farmland, timber, construction sites for residential and

Wetlands located near urban areas, like the San Francisco Bay National Wildlife Refuge, provide popular destinations for hikers, cyclists, bird watchers, and others seeking the respite of a natural setting close to home. They are also important venues for environmental education programs. Photo by John and Karen Hollingsworth, courtesy U.S. Fish and Wildlife Service.

commercial building. To generate the political will necessary to defend these landscapes on a national scale required a shared recognition that wetlands depletion also imposed significant financial *costs* on society. Not until the loss of wetlands was framed as an economic problem did the federal government act in a concerted manner. For the public to tolerate, if not actively favor, wetlands conservation and restoration, the costs and benefits of preservation and reclamation had to be elucidated. Environmental and natural resource economists had to clarify how the ecological services provided by wetlands—such as their ability to filter water and minimize flooding and storm damage—were crucial to society. If wetlands were lost, those natural functions would have to be replaced by costly water treatment and sewage disposal facilities, flood control structures, and water resource development projects. This recognition did not sweep the country overnight, but increasing numbers of people not

The visitors center at the Patuxent National Wildlife Research Refuge in Laurel, Maryland, showcases the environmental education efforts undertaken by the Fish and Wildlife Service at wetland reserves across the country. Photo by Rob Shallenberger, courtesy U.S. Fish and Wildlife Service.

otherwise predisposed toward an environmentalist agenda eventually came to see the health of wetlands as a matter of taxpayer concern.

From the standpoint of public policy, maintenance of ecological services came to form an essential rationale for the protection of wetlands. A secondary objective—but one nonetheless contributing to the general climate of acceptance for government intervention—was retention of the aesthetic and recreational values associated with swamps and marshes. Hunters, anglers, and commercial trappers had long haunted these settings, but the swelling ranks of nonconsumptive outdoors enthusiasts also began arguing that wetlands should be preserved because they provided relatively unspoiled retreats. This was especially true in the Southeast, where there were fewer remaining areas that offered such "natural" escapes. Thus, places like the Great Dismal Swamp, Okefenokee Swamp, Big Cypress Swamp, and the Everglades became treasured recreational havens. The region's numerous river swamps—such as the long and narrow wet forests found along South Carolina's Santee and Congaree rivers—have offered the most accessible wilderness-like experiences for the South's rural and urban populations alike. But the same held true throughout most of the nation: as the demand for outdoor recreational opportunities grew incessantly after the early 1960s, wetlands gained ever-increasing popularity among the general public. With interest in environmental education also escalating, the abundance and diversity of flora and fauna found in wooded swamps proved to be a powerful attraction to citizens longing to explore the natural histories of undeveloped landscapes.

CHAPTER FOUR

Regulating Wetlands

A lthough the Fish and Wildlife Service had carefully inventoried the nation's wetlands and had managed a choice set of marshes and swamps protected in its National Wildlife Refuge System, broader public safeguards came about first at the state level, as exemplified by the wetlands protection legislation adopted by Massachusetts in 1963, Rhode Island in 1965, Connecticut in 1969, New Jersey, Maryland, and Georgia in 1970, and New York two years later. The federal government did not step in to protect wetlands until 1972. Prior to that time, property owners and public agencies could alter or destroy these landscapes with little or no interference from Washington.

The Army Corps of Engineers had regulated activities that threatened commercial navigation in the nation's rivers and coastal waters since the enactment of the 1899 River and Harbor Act. When Congress passed the Water Pollution Control Act amendments of 1972, wetlands protection advocates latched onto the legislation's Section 404, which charged the Corps with regulating the discharge of dredged and fill material into the nation's waters. The Army engineers, however, resisted applying this new permit requirement to wetlands, cleaving instead to the traditional and far narrower definition of "navigable waters" as a rationale for limiting the scope of its policing authority to the rivers, lakes, and intracoastal waterways actually plied by commercial shippers. Several environmental organizations, led by the Natural Resources Defense Council, challenged the agency in federal court, arguing that it was Congress's intent to safeguard the overall quality of the nation's waters, a goal that required controlling pollution at its source. It therefore followed, the litigants contended, that Congress expected the Corps's regulatory authority to extend beyond navigable waterways to include their adjacent wetlands, tributaries, and headwaters. Ultimately, the U.S. District Court for the District of Columbia agreed, ruling in 1975 that the Corps must enlarge its permit program to encompass "all waters of the United States." The judicial decision did not quell the apprehensions of the regulation's opponents, who continued to debate the wisdom of this expanded federal program. When Congress superseded the 1972 legislation with the Clean Water Act of 1977, it voted to retain the Corps's broadened Section 404 permit jurisdiction but to streamline the application process by granting certain exemptions for "normal" forestry, farming, and ranching operations.

The 404 program requires the Army Corps of Engineers to evaluate the impacts of proposed development projects on wetlands, taking into account the comments provided by the Environmental Protection Agency (EPA), Fish and Wildlife Service, appropriate state agencies, and interested members of the public. The law encourages permit applicants to avoid and minimize impacts on wetlands wherever possible. Should the impacts of the proposed projects be deemed significantly harmful, the Corps has the option of denying the permit, requiring that the project be modified to diminish its damage, or mandating mitigation through the restoration, protection, and/or creation of wetlands that are equivalent in type and function to those being destroyed. Although it has only rarely exercised its authority, EPA is empowered to veto any Section 404 permit that it considers to have been ill-advisedly approved by the Corps.

The federal regulation of wetlands generated widespread support in some quarters and significant anxiety in others. Such polarization came as little surprise, given the mixed receptions that have historically greeted federal regulatory efforts in the United States. As if on cue, property rights advocates reflexively opposed the 404 program because it threatened to restrict the freedom of wetlands owners to develop or alter their property as they wished. This was no small matter. Roughly 75 percent of all wetlands in the contiguous United States were privately owned, and they directly or indirectly affected the broader public good through their impact on water quality and supply, the severity of flood and storm damage, and biological diversity. The fact that the benefits of protecting and maintaining wetlands have tended to accrue to society at large rather than to individual landowners only served to complicate matters further. Wetlands preservation has historically required active government intervention to overcome market forces that tilt sharply in favor of conversion.

The philosophical divisions over the merits of federal wetlands regulation per se did little to help calm the complaints arising from variations in the government's own legal identification and delineation of wetlands. Prior to the assumption of federal regulatory responsibilities, neither scientists nor bureaucrats had established consensus guidelines for determining the precise boundaries of wetlands. The absence of exact certainty about where to draw the lines on a map allowed different government agencies to adopt different criteria. These administrative inconsistencies bred confusion and suspicion.

Three elements lie at the heart of wetlands identification and delineation: hydrology (the presence of water at or near the land's surface), vegetation (the presence of plants capable of existing in saturated soils), and soils (the presence of anaerobic, or oxygen-deprived, soils that result from prolonged saturation). Because wetlands are neither well drained nor permanently flooded, they occupy the transitional territory between land and water. Although many sites are obviously swampy, others may appear as dry land during long stretches of time. This has led to misunderstandings among landowners whose common sense tells them that their boots should get muddy whenever they walk across a wetland. The vast diversity of wetland types that exists in nature, in addition to the technical difficulty of

In 1995, legal scholars Oliver A. Houck and Michael Rolland observed that:

"*Wetlands regulation may be the most controversial issue in environmental law. It pits America's most biologically-productive and most rapidly-diminishing ecosystems against rights of private ownership and property development in more than 10,000 individual permit decisions a year.*"

identifying sometimes where a wetland starts and an upland ends, contributed to inconsistencies in different federal manuals. The definitional variations were further exacerbated by the purposes for which each set of standards was devised: to provide legal definitions for regulation, or technical definitions for scientific investigation, or fish and wildlife management definitions for conservation.

The flames of this controversy fed on dissimilarities in how four agencies in particular—the Army Corps of Engineers, Environmental Protection Agency, Fish and Wildlife Service, and Soil Conservation Service (renamed the Natural Resources Conservation Service in 1994)—have defined and delineated wetlands. These differences arose from the variations in the agencies' histories, missions, viewpoints, and constituency groups. The Soil Conservation Service (in 1985), EPA (in 1987), and the Corps (in 1987) each issued its own distinct wetlands delineation manual. With both wetlands and property rights advocates calling for clarification, and with public confidence in the Section 404 permit process a matter of concern, the four agencies created a National Wetlands Policy Forum to hammer out a common standard. In 1989, the Corps, EPA, FWS, and Department of Agriculture (on behalf of the Soil Conservation Service) jointly published a revised set of guidelines that proved to be significantly more liberal in the classification of wetlands than the Corps's 1987 manual. The interagency document generated widespread complaints from various commercial interests and private landowners, which prompted the George H. W. Bush administration to propose a more restrictive manual in 1991. The president's action triggered an avalanche of countervailing complaints from conservationists and environmental organizations, who charged that the new manual would remove federal protection from about half of the nation's remaining wetlands. As a result, the proposed changes were dropped, and the Corps and EPA—the agencies ultimately responsible for enforcing and overseeing the Section 404 program—reverted to using the Army engineers' 1987 manual, which has since remained the standard.

The regulatory framework ushered in by the Federal Water Pollution Control Act amendments of 1972 found the forest industry siding with oil, gas, real estate, and other developers who worried that the Section 404 permit program could harm them economically by prohibiting or restricting their activities on properties identified as wetlands or by

Earthmoving equipment, like this 1940 Caterpillar D4 tractor, enabled the building of hundreds of thousands of miles of roads on private and public woodlands after World War II. During the 1970s, the timber industry campaigned vigorously for Section 404 permit exemptions for road construction in forested wetlands. Forest History Society Photo Collection.

delaying their activities through the time required to evaluate applications and issue permits. These interest groups were well aware that environmental organizations were pressuring the Corps to enlarge its jurisdictional authority, and they took full advantage of the opportunity afforded by the official public discussion period in summer 1975 to voice their opinions about the agency's revised interim rules. Timber company representatives were particularly anxious to learn whether a Section 404 permit would be required for forest road construction. Many industry representatives wanted routine road-building activities to be exempted. Alternatively, they argued for the adoption of statewide "general permits," which would cover all forest road construction that complied with state forestry and hydraulics standards.

In 1976, the Society of American Foresters established a task force on water quality to consider future actions on federal wetlands regulation. The society's leadership was concerned that the new permit application process would encumber such forestry practices as site preparation, reforestation, thinning, and harvesting operations, as well as road construction and maintenance. Wetlands had become a matter of grave concern to foresters, the society contended; the court-ordered expansion of the Corps's Section 404 regulatory program threatened to encompass many "highly productive forests and may comprise the majority of forest land in specific areas." The Society of American Foresters report warned that the new requirements might "preclude many forest management activities or reduce management options or opportunities" and force timber companies to obtain permits for minor forest drainage projects and for basic road construction in wetlands. Arguing that common silvicultural activities should not be regulated, the foresters called upon Congress to limit the Corps's jurisdictional authority.

The contentious wrangling over Section 404 regulations involved strongly held sets of values. Sensing the need for long-term data to help inform these deliberations, the Fish and Wildlife Service established the National Wetlands Inventory Project in 1974 to track the health of wetlands and systematically update the baseline of scientific information on their status through detailed maps, which were produced on a state-by-state basis by evaluating both historical information and contemporary aerial photographs, soil data, and field observations. FWS analysts detected a significant drop in the rate of wetlands loss following the establishment of the Section 404 regulatory program. In the 20 years from the mid-1950s to the mid-1970s, more than 9 million acres of wetlands had disappeared in the contiguous United States, an average loss of 458,000 acres per year. FWS estimated that the annual loss rate fell to about 290,000 acres between the mid-1970s and mid-1980s, when the nation's wetlands total declined by some 2.6 million acres. Agency analysts also noted a shift in the amount of wetlands sacrificed to farm expansions: agriculture accounted for 87 percent of the wetlands conversions that occurred from the mid-1950s to mid-1970s, but that percentage dropped to 54 during the next 10-year period. Because of intensified government protection efforts and improved land management techniques among many private property owners, the picture grew even brighter between 1986 and 1997, when FWS placed the net loss of wetlands at 644,000 acres, or an annual loss rate of 58,500 acres.

CHAPTER FIVE

Best Management Practices

Congress addressed the nation's water quality problems in the early 1970s by focusing on one of the most significant yet manageable threats: contaminants released from specific, identifiable outlets, such as municipal and industrial drainpipes. These point sources of pollution, as they were called, invited the application of technological fixes as a remedy. Thus, the Water Pollution Control Act amendments of 1972 incorporated such concepts as "best available technology" and "best practicable control technology" in establishing its regulatory requirements. When the 1977 Clean Water Act amended Section 404 to address nonpoint sources of pollution (such as the generalized runoff from farm fields, construction sites, and golf courses), it recognized that specific pollution control technologies would not be enough. A broader approach was needed, one that would minimize the release of water contaminants by establishing realistic standards of operation. In articulating that new approach, the Clean Water Act introduced a new term into law: best management practices (BMPs). The federal government soon issued several basic, nationwide BMPs, although most BMPs were envisioned to be regionally specific. Accordingly, in the 1980s the states began developing their own BMPs keyed to their own circumstances. Some states made compliance mandatory, others made it voluntary, yet in all instances there was a shared expectation that BMPs would be followed.

The concept of best management practices had appeared in publications in the United States since at least the early 1900s. The phrase did not enter into government parlance until 1975, however, when the Environmental Protection Agency issued nonpoint source pollution control regulations, which described BMPs as constituting "a practice, or combination of practices, that is determined by a state (or designated area-wide planning agency) after problem assessment, examination of alternative practices, and appropriate public participation to be the most effective, practicable (including technological, economic, and institutional considerations) means of preventing or reducing the amount

To reduce the impact of planting, tending, harvesting, and hauling activities in forested wetlands, equipment manufacturers have developed specialized machinery. One simple solution is to distribute a vehicle's weight over a broad area through the use of tracks or oversized tires. Courtesy Timberjack and Virginia Tech Department of Forestry.

of pollution generated by nonpoint sources to a level compatible with water quality goals." In 1977, EPA released guidelines on silvicultural BMPs pertaining to water quality management, and these principles came to play an important role in wetlands regulations associated with commercial timberlands. EPA also developed BMPs for agriculture and construction, occupational sectors similarly considered to be major nonpoint sources of water pollution. Because forestry BMPs were to be based on up-to-date silvicultural research, they were meant to evolve in accord with advancements in scientific knowledge and understanding. By relieving forestry operations from permit requirements only when they followed BMPs, the government sought to ensure that timber production would avoid or minimize direct or indirect damage to the wildlife habitat, hydrologic functions, and recreational values of wet forests.

The 1977 Clean Water Act introduced Section 404 permit exemptions for "normal" forestry, farming, and ranching operations. For silvicultural practices to be considered normal, the activities must be part of an established, ongoing operation for timber production (otherwise, a permit would be required, even if a forested wetland was being managed for wildlife or other nontimber objectives); the activities must not result in a "new use" of the land in question; and the activities must not impair the flow and circulation of the waters or reduce their reach. The legislation sought to exempt only routine, low-impact operations and to prevent the conversion of large tracts of wetlands into dry lands. Yielding to heavy lobbying by the industry, Congress specifically listed forest road construction and maintenance. To clarify this potentially tricky exemption, in 1982 the Corps issued BMPs that called on loggers and timber resource managers to limit the size of their forest roads, minimize stream crossings, design culverts and bridges to accommodate floodwaters, avoid shellfish beds and waterfowl breeding habitat, and not impair endangered and threatened species and their critical habitats.

The forest industry objected to the Corps's creation of BMPs because they would constitute a blanket, nationwide standard. Better, it argued, to rely on state BMPs, which promised to reflect more accurately the diverse physiographic, technical, economic, and political characteristics found across the continent. The viability of this approach gained strength as more states developed and refined their own BMPs in the 1980s and 1990s. Meanwhile, in 1986, the Corps and EPA elucidated the exemption of farm and forest roads from Section 404 permits: the agencies stated that so long as the roads were intended to be used solely for silvicultural or agricultural purposes and followed 15 BMPs, they would be exempted, even if they were incidentally used for other activities.

To provide the technical information necessary to create or refine the state BMPs, the National Council of the Paper Industry for Air and Stream Improvement (NCASI) initiated a $400,000 annual research program on the environmental impacts of silviculture on forested wetlands. Having functioned as the forest industry's environmental research arm since 1943, NCASI now sought to evaluate the hypothesis that wet forests could be managed for timber production in ways that maintained the ecological functions and values of wetlands. Its Forest Wetlands Program awarded over $4 million to independent researchers (most of them university based) during its years of operation from 1989 to 1998. More than 100 research publications sprang from that effort. In 1998, NCASI merged the Forest Wetlands Program's ongoing, long-term field studies with its broader Sustainable Forestry Research Program, where wetlands research continued to be funded at a reduced level.

The Forest Service and other entities also supported research associated with silvicultural practices in wetlands. One area of special concern during the early 21st century has been the impact of timber operations on water quality. Although BMPs were intended to minimize nonpoint source pollution, the science underpinning the state-developed guidelines had been derived largely from studies undertaken in upland situations. More targeted research within wet forests sought to improve BMPs, with the goal of advancing commercial timber production that would be both sustainable and minimally compromising of wetland values and functions.

CHAPTER SIX

A Partnership in Conservation

Notwithstanding their victory in securing regulatory exemptions for normal silvicultural activities under the Clean Water
Act, forest industry advocates remained vigilant, as they understood that the definition of "normal" silvicultural activities was ambiguous
and therefore subject to future debate. Legal interpretations of the Clean
Water Act in the late 1970s and 1980s upheld most forestry-related exemptions from Section 404 regulations. Cutting trees and removing the timber
and organic debris from a forested wetland did not require a permit.
However, any mechanized land clearing that disturbed an area's root system or redeposited soil or vegetation on site (such as the use of bulldozers
to push earth around or to rake organic debris into rows for burning) would
be prohibited without a permit.

Forestry officials were aware that the Fish and Wildlife Service inventories had documented an uptick in the loss rate for forested wetlands since
the mid-1970s, despite a drop in the combined rate of loss for all wetland
categories during that time period. Wet forests had represented 54 percent
of all freshwater wetlands lost from the mid-1950s to the mid-1970s. That
rate jumped to 95 percent during the next decade, when about 3.4 million
acres of forested wetlands was destroyed. The heaviest declines occurred
in the southern states of Arkansas, Louisiana, Mississippi, Florida, Georgia,
South Carolina, and North Carolina. Concern about the relentless damage being inflicted upon North America's largest productive hardwood
region led industrial foresters, forestry educators, and forestry professionals from federal and state agencies to form the Southern Hardwood
Coordinating Committee in 1975. It was unclear whether the continuing
net loss of forested wetlands would hold any implications for the future of

Managed tree farms became increasingly popular in the Southeast during the second half of the 20th century. These tractors are preparing a seedbed for a new pine plantation near Panama City, Florida. Photo by Daniel O. Todd for the U.S. Forest Service, Forest History Society Photo Collection.

Section 404 regulatory exemptions for silviculture, but it certainly helped keep the question before Congress and the federal courts.

In general, environmental activists endorsed sustained timber harvesting within wet forests because it provided landowners with economic returns from their properties in a manner that maintained wetland values and functions. Many environmentalists, however, objected to the timber companies' use of Section 404 silvicultural exemptions to harvest hardwoods in swamp forests and then convert these naturally occurring wetlands into managed pine plantations—a practice that replaced mixed-species, mixed-age forests with single-species, even-aged pine fields. In searching for a test case to challenge this practice, the Environmental Defense Fund

(EDF; the organization changed its name to Environmental Defense in 2000) selected the Weyerhaeuser Company's operations in eastern North Carolina. In 1991, EDF and four other environmental organizations filed suit against Weyerhaeuser, EPA, and the Corps of Engineers for alleged violations of the Clean Water Act in the management of the property known as the Parker Tract. Weyerhaeuser was North Carolina's largest private landowner, and it had acquired the 11,000-acre timber reserve on the Albemarle-Pamlico peninsula near Plymouth in 1967 and 1969. The land represented the last remnant of what once was the 100,000-acre East Dismal Swamp, which had covered most of the low-lying peninsula. With the majority of this forested wetland long since converted to agriculture, the Parker Tract functioned as a regional oasis for woodland wildlife, including black bear, gray fox, and several threatened reptiles, amphibians, and migratory songbirds.

At the time Weyerhaeuser took ownership, the pine and mixed hardwood stands had already been partially drained by canals bordering three sides of the tract, as well as by deep ditches that paralleled the 24 miles of forest roads crisscrossing the property. Weyerhaeuser maintained this drainage system and dug additional ditches, all the while adhering to the regulatory requirements in place at the time. From the timber company's standpoint, the Corps and EPA had considered all of its silvicultural practices on the Parker Tract to be "normal" and therefore exempt from Section 404 permit requirements.

The plaintiffs disagreed, contending that Weyerhaeuser's conversion of the natural, mixed-hardwood swamp into a managed pine plantation did not represent normal silvicultural operations and should not have been allowed without a 404 permit. This matter held special significance, EDF argued, because the Parker Tract provided essential habitat for an array of threatened and endangered plants and animals and played a pivotal role in maintaining the water quality of the Albemarle Sound. Moreover, the environmentalists maintained that Weyerhaeuser's discharge of dredged and fill material into the nonriverine swamp forest directly violated the Clean Water Act. They invested heavily in this litigation, hoping for a far-reaching payoff: the establishment of a legal precedent that would curb the loss of prime forested wetlands throughout the Southeast.

Following months of debate and legal maneuvering, EPA's Region IV ruled in 1994 that Weyerhaeuser's operations—the mechanical plowing,

This aerial photograph of the Parker Tract in North Carolina shows the juxtaposition of mixed-hardwood swamp forest and managed pine fields. Photo by Gary Darby, courtesy of Weyerhaeuser Company.

bedding, field ditching, and forest road construction—constituted normal silvicultural practices and therefore needed no 404 permit. Moreover, EPA determined that Weyerhaeuser's plan to convert the mixed-hardwood swamp into a pine plantation would not constitute a "new use" of the land, meaning that this activity, too, was exempted. The agency based its conclusions on Weyerhaeuser's management of the Parker Tract since 1978 (the date when Section 404 permits would have first been required there) and found that most of the major modifications to the swampland, including the drainage system, were already in place and that the landowners had run afoul of no pre-1978 law or regulation in undertaking these modifications. EPA left open what types of future site preparation would be exempted from Section 404, and thus it set up a process to make this determination. The collaborative process involved EPA officials and representatives from relevant federal and state agencies, environmental organizations, foresters, and other interested parties.

As a result of those interactions, EPA and the Corps of Engineers issued a special set of guidelines in November 1995, titled "Application of Best Management Practices to Mechanical Silvicultural Site Preparation Activities for the Establishment of Pine Plantations in the Southeast." The forested wetlands BMPs for mechanical site preparation and harvesting identified specific activities that either did or did not require a Section 404 permit. Recognizing the relative rarity and fragility of certain types of wetland environments, the guidelines required 404 permits for mechanical site preparation in any of the following landscape categories: permanently flooded, intermittently exposed, and semipermanently flooded wetlands; riverine bottomland hardwood wetlands; white cedar swamps; Carolina bay wetlands; and barrier island wetlands. All other types of wet forests—essentially those that were seasonally or temporarily flooded, or those already in existing silvicultural sites—would be exempted, so long as the mechanical site preparation and harvesting adhered to BMPs.

The EPA-Corps memorandum identified mechanical silvicultural site preparation activities as including "shearing, raking, ripping, chopping, windrowing, piling, and other similar physical methods used to cut, break apart, or move logging debris following harvest." Among the BMPs were practices that minimized soil disturbances, avoided excessive soil compaction, and limited erosion and runoff; avoided storage and disposal of logging debris in streamside management zones; maintained the contour of the site; and minimized off-site water quality impacts.

One month later, in December 1995, the environmental organizations agreed to drop their lawsuit after Weyerhaeuser entered into an interactive conservation partnership with the Environmental Defense Fund. In addition to sharing scientific and economic information, they were ordered to work together to develop management criteria for the Parker Tract that would allow Weyerhaeuser to continue its forestry operations while protecting wildlife habitat, water quality, unique wetland sites, and rare plants. After 18 months of deliberations, the parties agreed that the most viable swamp forest remnants within the Parker Tract would be placed in a 500-acre preserve, within which no trees would be harvested. Weyerhaeuser set aside an additional 1,000 acres as a temporary reserve, where it promised to forgo any logging unless future research demonstrated that such actions would have a beneficial impact on selected songbirds and reptiles. The management plan called for 820 acres to be devoted to hardwood

timber production and regeneration, with systematic scientific studies undertaken on wildlife populations. Another 680 acres would be managed for
either pine or hardwoods, and the remaining 8,000 acres would be managed for loblolly pine sawtimber, following BMPs for planting, thinning,
and harvesting. In their jointly authored July 1997 report, *A Partnership
in Conservation*, Weyerhaeuser and Environmental Defense Fund officials
proclaimed their "hope that the Partnership will serve as a valuable model
not only for environmentally sensitive forest management, but also for con-
structive, scientifically sound cooperation between environmentalists and
the forest products industry."

Weyerhaeuser's tenacious legal defense elicited quiet applause from leaders throughout the forest industry, who had followed the lawsuit closely.
They understood that the relief they enjoyed from Section 404 regulations
could always be revoked by Congress or severely curtailed by the federal
courts. Although any questioning of the silvicultural exemptions raised
anxiety levels within the industry, events during the 1980s and early 1990s—
including the Parker Tract test case litigation—led many timber company
officials to worry that overly aggressive resistance to federal regulations
might prove counterproductive because public appreciation of wetlands
had continued to grow. Recognizing this trend, John Toliver of the USDA
Forest Service argued in the May 1993 issue of the *Journal of Forestry*,
"As stewards of our nation's forests, we must follow appropriate silvicultural practices and approved best management practices to maintain,
enhance, and if possible restore wetland forests. Otherwise, these productive, multiple-resource sites may no longer retain their functions and values
as wetlands, or they may be placed under preservation programs that limit
our use of them." The forest industry, he implied, had to do a better job of
regulating itself if it did not want the government regulating its actions for
it. The American Forest and Paper Association created the Forest Industry
Wetlands Task Force in the early 1990s to address this very issue by developing strategy options.

Some forest products companies took the additional step of engaging in
public education through the publication of brochures and informational
ads, the development of visitors centers and interpretative hiking trails on
selected properties, the sponsorship of public lectures and forestry muse-
ums, and the like. Part of this effort involved showcasing what they were
doing to protect forested wetlands and making the case that well-planned

commercial forestry could be compatible with wetlands preservation. The International Paper Company, for example, noted in one of its public-oriented brochures that "unlike agriculture or development, you don't have to drain or otherwise alter a wetland area to grow and harvest timber in it. In fact, keeping wetland areas economically productive through forest production is one of the best ways to ensure it won't be converted to some other use, like a shopping center or a residential development."

CHAPTER SEVEN

Supreme Court Rulings

E nvironmental policy may not have been a deciding factor in the
2000 presidential election, but that only raised the level of antic-
ipation among people concerned with the future of wetlands
protection, no matter what stand they took on the matter. Their anticipa-
tion spiked in January 2001, only a few days before Bill Clinton turned the
White House over to George W. Bush, when the Supreme Court issued a
landmark ruling on the federal regulation of isolated ponds and wetlands.
The Court resolved a suit that had been filed a decade earlier by the Solid
Waste Agency of Northern Cook County (SWANCC), a consortium of 23
small municipalities outside Chicago that sought to develop a permanent
disposal site for their baled nonhazardous waste. SWANCC had purchased
a 533-acre former sand and gravel pit in Illinois for this purpose, and it
had little trouble obtaining the necessary state and local permits. Getting
a green light from the federal government, however, was another matter.
After being abandoned in 1960, the property's old excavation trenches
eventually filled with water, transforming them into a thriving, if unlikely,
habitat for more than 100 species of migrating birds, including a large population of great blue herons. Because the proposed landfill would eliminate
these ponds—and with them the migratory bird habitat—the Army Corps
of Engineers denied the consortium's Section 404 permit application. The
agency's decision flowed logically from the 1986 "migratory bird rule,"
which had charged the Army engineers with protecting isolated wetlands
used by migratory birds, given the birds' contributions to interstate commerce via the tourism associated with bird watching and hunting. SWANCC
sued the Corps, arguing that the government had no right under the Clean
Water Act to regulate wetlands unconnected to navigable waters.

The Supreme Court concurred. In *Solid Waste Agency of Northern Cook County v. Army Corps of Engineers*, the justices ruled five to four that Congress had intended the Clean Water Act to apply only to waters that were themselves navigable or that were adjacent to navigable waters and their tributaries. Thus, isolated wetlands—such as prairie potholes, vernal pools, cypress domes, wet meadows, bogs, vast stretches of Alaskan tundra, and certain forested swamps—were not subject to federal regulation based solely upon the interstate commerce clause. In striking down the migratory bird rule, the Court ordered the Corps to return to its 1974 definition of "navigable waters," which basically restricted the agency's jurisdiction to waters subject to the ebb and flow of the tide and usable for transportation and commerce. According to the Court, the Army engineers' regulatory authority was restricted to "actually navigable waters, their tributaries, and wetlands adjacent to each." This loss of federal protection for

This long-abandoned sand and gravel pit in northwestern Cook County, Illinois, was at the center of a legal battle decided by the U.S. Supreme Court. *Chicago Tribune* photo by John Handley. All rights reserved. Used with permission.

isolated wetlands was generally welcomed by commercial interests and vehemently opposed by conservation and environmental advocates. The Association of State Wetlands Managers, for example, estimated that the Court's decision threatened to leave 30 to 79 percent of the nation's total wetland acreage outside the Section 404 permit program.

Where federal jurisdiction receded, it was left to state and local governments to protect wetlands, but their willingness and ability to accomplish this weighty task remained problematic, given the cost requirements for staffing, training, and enforcement. Congress was thus confronted with the question of whether it should amend the Clean Water Act to state unequivocally that Section 404 applied to all the nation's waters, including isolated waters and wetlands, or whether it should replace the 404 program altogether by enacting even broader water and wetlands regulatory provisions. The legislators also had the option of increasing allocations to EPA's annual state wetlands grant program, which assisted the states in establishing and implementing their own programs.

The National Academy of Sciences added its own wrinkle to this political debate in June 2001 when it issued a report questioning the ecological viability of artificial wetlands, which in turn raised doubts about the efficacy of the federal government's wetlands mitigation program. Launched in 1989, the mitigation program had allowed landowners to fill in natural wetlands if they agreed either to restore degraded wetlands or create artificial wetlands elsewhere. The program called for 1.8 acres of artificial or restored wetlands for every acre of natural wetlands destroyed. Many of these substitute wetlands, however, had been delayed or were never finished, and those that were completed failed to match the ecological functions of natural wetlands. The academy report cited a lack of appropriate oversight and monitoring by the federal regulatory agencies, most particularly the Corps. Sweeping changes were required, according to the scientific panel, if the government wanted to achieve no net loss of wetlands, which had been the federal wetlands policy objective since the first Bush administration. The academy recommended that U.S. wetlands policy take into account the fact that created wetlands were poor substitutes for natural ones.

The fine-tuning of the federal government's wetlands mitigation program was a matter of no small import, but it paled in comparison with the potential reduction in the Section 404 protections augured by the Supreme

Court ruling. How the Court's decision would play out remained an open question. The ruling generated extensive press coverage and intensified congressional lobbying both for and against legislative attempts to weaken wetlands regulation. The SWANCC decision came at the end of the Clinton presidency. The succeeding Bush administration then waited nearly two years to respond officially, releasing a nonbinding "advance notice of proposed rulemaking" in January 2003, together with a "guidance document" directed to Army Corps of Engineers and EPA field agents, who were instructed that "isolated waters" that were not navigable and were contained within a single state (waters, that is, that were intrastate rather than interstate) no longer fell within Section 404 permit jurisdiction. The document further inhibited the 404 program by requiring the field agents to obtain "headquarters approval" prior to issuing noncompliance citations. In essence, it served as an enforcement ban until the actual rule making on what did or did not constitute an "isolated wetland." Despite the protests of hunters, anglers, and environmentalists, the guidelines went beyond the Supreme Court's stated rationales by declaring "endangered species" and "crop irrigation" to be insufficient grounds for protecting wetlands.

The Bush administration's proposed rule changes unleashed a highly charged, bipartisan opposition. Environmentalists and politically conservative hunting and fishing organizations formed a chorus of complaints about the attempt to narrow federal authority over the nation's wetlands. EPA received an outpouring of some 133,000 public comments, more than 99 percent of which opposed the rule change. This overwhelming response induced an about-face on the part of the White House. In December 2003, the president reaffirmed his commitment to "no net loss of wetlands" and put on hold any formal changes in Section 404 jurisdictional regulations.

As the electoral campaign gained momentum in spring 2004, the leading Democratic candidate, Senator John F. Kerry, focused harsh criticism on President Bush's environmental record. Although the environment remained a subordinate campaign issue for both parties, public opinion polls nevertheless indicated a deep-rooted interest in the matter, enough to prompt President Bush to make an Earth Day (April 22) appearance at a coastal marsh near his parents' house in southern Maine. There he defended his record and announced the administration's plan to go beyond the no-net-loss-of-wetlands goal by setting a nationwide target of increasing the net amount of wetlands by 3 million acres within five years. Bush's choice of making wetlands stand for his environmental approach in general reflected the administration's keen appreciation of the importance this issue had gained among environmentally aware Americans. Over the past 50 years, there had been an inverse relationship between public appreciation of wetlands and total wetland acreage in the United States: as the latter declined, the former increased. The shrinking resource base, the expanding scientific understanding of wetlands, and the general realization of the landscape's ecological services all contributed to an elevated public appreciation.

These public attitudes coexisted, however, with Americans' long-standing emphasis on private property rights and a culture that has perpetually resisted government regulation. The continuing uncertainty about the extent of federal jurisdiction of wetlands under Section 404 of the Clean Water Act exaggerated this tension. When the Supreme Court ruled in June 2006 on two consolidated cases—*Rapanos v. United States* and *Carabell v. United States Army Corps of Engineers*—the need for clarifying legislation was underlined. Both cases involved long-standing property rights disputes in Michigan: John Rapanos had wanted to construct a shopping mall on 54 acres of wetlands bordering a nonnavigable tributary that emptied into a river, and Keith Carabell had been fighting the federal government for 18 years to acquire the permits necessary to build condominiums on approximately 16 acres of forested wetlands about a mile from Lake St. Clair.

The Supreme Court's five-four decision failed to produce a clear-cut victory for either property rights advocates or wetlands advocates because both cases were sent back to the federal appeals court. The justices also did not clarify which waters were protected under the Clean Water Act. Four judges argued that only "permanent, standing, or continuously flowing" water bodies were to be protected—an interpretation that would have excluded most wetlands and all seasonal streams. Four other judges expressed the opposite view—that the Clean Water Act protected all the nation's waters, including its wetlands. Justice Anthony Kennedy cast the deciding vote, but the ambiguity of his position—that protected water bodies must have a "significant nexus" with a navigable waterway—just ensured ongoing regulatory uncertainty and future legal disputes.

Under the decision, the Corps of Engineers retained its authority to make technical determinations about what wetlands fell within Section 404 jurisdictional boundaries, but the Court instructed the agency that regulatory jurisdiction must be based on a "significant nexus" between a wetland and a navigable waterway. The Court, in effect, limited the reach of federal wetlands regulation, albeit not as much as property rights advocates desired. Nevertheless, the decision leaned toward a narrowing of Section 404 jurisdiction, which was to be limited to "relatively permanent, standing or continuously flowing bodies of water" that constitute "geographic features," a ruling that raised concerns about the continued federal protection of seasonal wetlands.

By not defining "significant nexus," the justices failed to establish precise limits on the regulatory jurisdiction under the Clean Water Act. It was understood that if wetlands buffered a larger waterway (like a river or lake) against storms and floods, or if they filtered pollutants that might flow into those waterways, they could be protected. Actual definitions of how to determine what wetlands met this test were left to subsequent court cases, and spokespersons for property rights and environmental groups concurred that the Supreme Court's split decision would invite more lawsuits. The ruling also clarified the need for Congress to step in to resolve the matter. At the time of the 2006 ruling, Congress was considering a bill—the Clean Water Authority Restoration Act—that would assert unambiguously the Clean Water Act's intention of protecting all the nation's waters, navigable or isolated, permanent or seasonal.

CHAPTER EIGHT

The Ivory-billed Woodpecker

Throughout the history of American forested wetlands, debates and decisions tended to focus on the land—its use and disuse—or on the trees. In 2005, public attention turned to a single iconic bird, and to these wet landscapes as the last refuge of an extraordinary survivor. That April, a team of 17 scientists announced multiple sightings and sound recordings of the ivory-billed woodpecker in the swamp forests of eastern Arkansas. The third-largest woodpecker in the world and one of North America's ornithological wonders, the ivory-bill had long been presumed extinct. The last confirmed sighting had been 60 years before. The possibility that one or more of the birds survived gave this conservation story profound significance and considerable public appeal. The fact that observations had been made in the Bayou DeView section of the Cache River National Wildlife Refuge, in a remote wooded swamp thick with cypress, oak, and tupelo, intensified attention to the role of forested wetlands as vital biological habitats.

The Big Woods region covers about 550,000 acres between Memphis and Little Rock, making it the largest expanse of bottomland hardwood forest in the Mississippi River Delta north of Louisiana's Atchafalaya River. It represents a fragment of the ancient floodplain forest that had once blanketed some 8 million acres in Arkansas alone. About 300,000 acres of the Big Woods is contiguous, while its remaining lands form forested islands adrift in a sea of farm fields.

This dense swampland is a likely home for the elegant ivory-bill. The woodpecker's size and dramatic coloration led early settlers to call it the "Lord God Bird." Adults grow to about 20 inches in length, with 30- to 33-inch wingspans and imposing, chisellike bills. Males have a prominent red crest; the females' crests are black. Both have jet-black bodies and wings sporting distinctive white patches on their trailing edges. Using their great bills, they feed on grubs living under bark too thick for any other bird species to dislodge, and this specialization makes them dependent upon large expanses of mature swamp forests, which provide a succession of standing dead trees. A slow breeder, the bird was never superabundant, yet naturalists such as John James Audubon reported widespread findings of ivory-billed woodpeckers in lowland primary forests across the Southeast. Prior to the fragmentation of the nation's far-reaching bottomland forests, the ivory-bill's range extended from Texas to North Carolina and from Missouri to Florida and on south to Cuba. After the Civil War, however, land clearing and the overhunting of ivory-bills for feathers and trophies (Indians had long coveted the woodpecker's white bill, which Euramerican hunters eagerly traded as souvenirs) decimated the population. By the turn of the 20th century, the ivory-bill had become the rarest woodpecker in North America. Continued logging and clearing of the South's old-growth swamp forests further reduced the bird's numbers, which perversely increased its value among collectors.

During the early 20th century, sightings continued within the imposing Tensas swamp in northeastern Louisiana. As late as 1907, even President Theodore Roosevelt had been able to observe three ivory-bills during a hunting trip to the area. Around 1900, however, railroads began bringing logging crews to this previously isolated forest reserve, allowing timber companies to work their way into the wooded lowlands from the north and the south. The Tensas swamp was spared from further logging in 1913 when the Singer Manufacturing Company purchased the 80,000-acre tract to hold as a preserve so that it might ensure a future supply of high-quality oak trees, which it used for its popular sewing-machine cabinets. The verdant, wildlife-filled lowland supported a mix of virgin and second-growth hardwoods. To ward off the harvesting of resources, the Singer Manufacturing Company declared the Tensas swamp a private refuge, prohibiting hunting and logging without its prior approval. Although modest levels of poaching occurred, the swamp forest—soon known as the Singer Tract—was effectively protected.

By the mid-1920s, the Singer Tract contained the most extensive expanse of old-growth bottomland forest in the Mississippi River delta. The Louisiana Department of Conservation leased the wildlife rights to the property in

In 1731, the colonial naturalist Mark Catesby published the first detailed account and illustration of the ivory-billed woodpecker. He called the bird the "Largest White-Bill Wood-Pecker" but described its bill as being "white as ivory." He commented on the bird's size, food preference, and remarkable ability to excavate nesting holes, as well as the trading of the bird's distinctive bills among Native Americans. Image from Mark Catesby, *The Natural History of Carolina, Florida, and the Bahama Islands* (1731), courtesy of Cullman Library, Smithsonian Institution Libraries.

1926 and managed it as a state refuge. The 10-year agreement included a clause reserving the Singer Manufacturing Company's right to develop the land or harvest its timber when the lease expired.

Meanwhile, ornithologists, who had mourned the extinction of the passenger pigeon in 1914 and the Carolina parakeet in 1918, questioned whether the ivory-billed woodpecker had suffered the same fate. When the founding director of the Cornell Laboratory of Ornithology, Arthur A. Allen, and his wife and fellow ornithologist, Elsa Guerdrum Allen, discovered a pair of ivory-bills near Florida's Taylor River in 1924, hopes rose, only to be dashed when two local taxidermists retraced the Allens' steps and (legally) shot the woodpeckers.

Debates about the status of the species resumed among ornithologists and birders until April 1932, when Louisiana state legislator Mason D. Spencer—under a special permit from the Louisiana Department of Conservation—shot a male ivory-bill in the general area of the Singer Tract to provide incontrovertible proof to skeptical state wildlife officials that the bird still existed. The rediscovery of the ivory-billed woodpecker became national news, and the ornithologists who rushed to the scene eventually found six more birds. The National Audubon Society moved quickly to pressure the Louisiana Department of Conservation to increase protection of the bird, which the agency did by assigning two additional wardens to patrol the area and by promising not to issue any more permits for collecting ivory-bills. Long-term concerns about the rare woodpecker remained acute, however, because the state's 10-year lease with the Singer Manufacturing Company stood to expire in November 1936.

In 1935, Arthur Allen led a four-person team from the Cornell Lab to the Singer Tract, where they located three ivory-bill nests. They proceeded to make the world's first motion pictures and sound recordings of the great woodpeckers. Despite the widely shared belief that the Tensas swamp might well be the nation's last ivory-bill stronghold, the Singer Manufacturing Company began turning its holdings over to lumber companies in 1937, eventually selling 6,000 acres to the Tendall Lumber Company and leasing the timber rights to the remaining 74,000 acres to the Chicago Mill and Lumber Company, which established a large sawmill in the nearby town of Tallulah. Conservationists were livid. They led a failed effort in 1940 to persuade Congress to purchase critical areas of the Singer Tract for the establishment of a national park. Although the Chicago Mill and Lumber

Company officials entered into negotiations with the Singer Sewing Machine Company, the state of Louisiana, the Fish and Wildlife Service, and the National Audubon Society, they ultimately refused to set aside lands or slow their harvesting. Indeed, when the demands for military supplies accelerated during World War II, so did the pace of their logging operations.

Concerned about the fate of what they feared might be the last ivory-bill, the National Audubon Society sent wildlife artist Don Eckelberry to the Singer Tract in April 1944 to draw this specimen before its nesting tree was felled. Working with Jesse Laird, a local man who had assisted the Cornell scientists with their 1930s fieldwork, Eckelberry observed and sketched the bird. This observation by Eckelberry and Laird became the last confirmed sighting of the ivory-billed woodpecker in the United States. The old-growth hardwoods of the Singer Tract were soon logged and made into tea chests, packing crates, and plywood gasoline tanks for the war effort. Although its mature forests were gone, the Singer Tract's regenerated swamplands were eventually incorporated into the Tensas River National Wildlife Refuge, which was created in 1980.

Sighting and photographing an ivory-billed woodpecker became a lifelong quest for a small but persistent circle of ornithologists and birders. Periodically, observations were reported from various forested wetlands in the South, but no photographs or other conclusive documentation was produced to substantiate these claims until the 2005 rediscovery in Arkansas. Anticipating a stampede of serious bird watchers and the merely curious once the news broke, federal and state agencies, conservation organizations, and university biologists conspired to keep the rediscovery secret for a year to allow unimpeded fieldwork and to ramp up protection of the woodpecker and its habitat. Toward that end, the Cache River National Wildlife Refuge set aside 5,000 acres as a new managed-access zone requiring research permits for entrance, the Nature Conservancy bought land in the Big Woods to expand the range of the protected habitat, and the Departments of Agriculture and Interior purchased development easements in adjacent forests and funded tree planting on refuge lands by private industry.

For decades, the ivory-billed woodpecker had been a symbol of loss, a reminder of the multifaceted costs of despoiling one of North America's most vibrant and biologically productive landscapes—the southern swamps and bottomland hardwood forests. In 2005, the ivory-bill became a

The Cache River National Wildlife Refuge gained international attention with the announced sightings of the ivory-billed woodpecker. The publicity also heightened awareness of the contributions forested wetlands make to biological diversity. Courtesy National Conservation Training Center Archives/Museum, U.S. Fish and Wildlife Service.

symbol of hope—a testament to the resilience of nature and the benefits of wetlands conservation. Later that same year, the destruction inflicted by Hurricanes Katrina and Rita on Texas, Louisiana, and Mississippi drove home another lesson: the importance of coastal wetlands for erosion control and storm protection.

Scientists and engineers had long argued that degradation of Gulf Coast wetlands could contribute to damage during a major storm. Louisiana contains about 40 percent of the United States' coastal wetlands outside Alaska but had, over the years, suffered about 80 percent of the nation's loss of those resources. Aerial reconnaissance following Hurricanes Katrina and Rita revealed stark contrasts between coastal areas where the marshes had been allowed to thrive and where the marshes had been compromised and pushed aside by development. The former areas were shielded from severe damage, while the latter were punished unmercifully and—all too often— left in tatters. Scientists later estimated that Katrina and Rita had destroyed some 64,000 acres of coastal wetlands, leaving inland areas more vulnerable to future storms. From the hope and inspiration of an extraordinary bird to the tragedy and loss from hurricanes, Americans had been reminded that swamps, marshes, and forested wetlands had a value to the nation that could not be replaced.

CHAPTER NINE

Looking to the Future

A mid the rising concern about the state of America's wetlands, the Fish and Wildlife Service published statistical findings in 2006 showing that, between 1998 and 2004, the contiguous United States had experienced its first measured net increase ever in wetland acreage. The total net gain was said to be 191,750 acres, an average annual accretion of nearly 32,000 acres. The reported reversal in the nation's long trend of wetlands losses seemed counterintuitive, however, because swamps, marshes, and bogs were still disappearing. (According to FWS, some 523,500 acres of natural wetlands were lost during this six-year period.) Skeptics characterized the small net gain as a bureaucratic sleight of hand—the current administration, they asserted, had merely expanded the definition of wetlands used for the aerial surveys, adding artificial ponds with surface areas under 20 acres to the mix. Using this broader set of criteria, FWS officials had found that pond inflation exceeded swamp and marshland depletion. Because these impoundments (which included golf course water hazards, ornamental lakes gracing new housing and commercial developments, mine reclamation reservoirs, and farm ponds) could be up to 30 feet deep and because they often lacked the successional vegetation and soils that provided the highly valued ecological functions of natural wetlands, the nation, in fact, continued to face a crisis in the decline of the quality and diversity of its wetlands. Even FWS cautioned that its own inventory had not assessed changes in wetland functions or quality—two essential elements that probably experienced reductions during this period.

Wetlands advocates from across the political spectrum responded quickly to the release of the FWS 2006 report, *Status and Trends of Wetlands in the Conterminous United States, 1998 to 2004*. The Theodore Roosevelt

Conservation Partnership (a coalition of organizations representing hunters, anglers, and conservationists), for example, criticized the inventory for ignoring the crucial questions of quality and condition. Simply counting acreage was not enough. The partnership emphasized that artificial water bodies "do not provide the same habitat, water cleansing, or flood control values" as do natural wetlands. The nation is continuing to lose important natural wetlands, it noted, and restoration and protection of those valuable resources must remain a priority conservation concern.

The attention and passion aroused by the Fish and Wildlife Service inventory surprised few people. It has been consistently difficult to achieve agreement about what constitutes the ideal federal wetlands policy, even as public appreciation of wetlands has grown ever stronger over the past half-century. The reasons stem from the long-standing ambivalence toward an ambiguous environment. The land dimension of wetlands invariably provokes discussion of property rights, while their water dimension (which transcends property boundaries through contributions to water quality and supply, public health, biodiversity, and recreation) invariably draws forth concern for public rights. That tension between private property and the public good has shaped the history of wetlands in America and will likely continue to shape its future. Moreover, the debate is now an international one. With global population projected to increase by some 2.5 billion people during the next 25 years, the demand for potable water will escalate accordingly, making the health of the world's wetlands no longer a luxury but a necessity for survival, especially for the tens of millions of people living in cities dependent upon wetland-fed streams and aquifers. Global climate change—which threatens wetlands via rising sea levels, altered precipitation patterns, and fluctuating temperatures—will only exacerbate these problems.

Ecological knowledge can inform efforts to delineate and restore wetlands, but it cannot settle the question of how regulatory systems should be fashioned or the extent to which these landscapes should be protected under the law. Ultimately, the contest over wetlands is neither a scientific nor a technical debate but a political one. To enlighten that political process, however, decision makers and American citizens must be informed of relevant scientific information and debates and their implications for policy choices.

The forest industry, like the larger society itself, has come a long way in recognizing the importance of these transitional ecosystems. The American Forest and Paper Association (AF&PA), which represents about 20 percent of the country's timber companies, is actively working to persuade the industry to change its management of forested wetlands. AF&PA has pushed to educate industry leaders and managers for the long run through its research programs and sustainable forestry initiative, and the association requires its members to adhere to state-established BMPs. The forest industry in general has argued that wetlands preservation and enhancement are strengthened through sound timber management, which is compatible with the maintenance of wetland values and functions and provides economic incentives for private landowners to retain their wetlands in forest cover. Some timber and paper companies acknowledge the importance of prime forested wetlands for fish and wildlife values by donating them to parks and wildlife reserves or, occasionally, entering into land exchanges. Examples of such transfers abound. The Georgia-Pacific Corporation did this in 1974, selling its 1,834 acres of land holdings in North Carolina's Camden County—part of the famed Great Dismal Swamp, which straddles the border between Virginia and North Carolina—to the Nature Conservancy. The Nature Conservancy then turned the land over to the Fish and Wildlife Service to manage as part of its wildlife refuge in this historic swamp. In 1993, the Potlatch Corporation exchanged nearly 41,000 acres of bottomland hardwoods along the White River in Arkansas for 17,625 acres of federal property in Idaho. The Arkansas land was added to the National Wildlife Refuge System (an area subsequently thought to provide ivory-billed woodpecker habitat), and Potlatch now manages the Idaho land—which was determined to have no significant wildlife or wetland values—for sustained-yield timber production.

Acknowledging the fact that property owners will continue to face federal regulations, many policy analysts see the need for additional market-based approaches to protect the nation's wetlands heritage in the future. Whatever the mechanisms employed—whether they be tax incentives, pollution fees, marketable permits, conservation easements, transfers of development rights, mitigation banking, or something else—society's challenge is how to relieve the ever-mounting economic pressures to convert privately held forested wetlands.

Recognizing the ecological and scenic value of its 6,090-acre property on Lewis Island, near the mouth of Georgia's Altamaha River, the Georgia-Pacific Corporation sold the land for less than half its value to the Nature Conservancy in 1973. Today, Lewis Island can be enjoyed by the public as part of the Altamaha State Wildlife Management Area. Forest History Society Photo Collection.

Market-oriented approaches have their advantages, but just as science is limited in its ability to resolve society's conflicts over wetland environments, so too is the market limited in fully resolving these disagreements. That is because markets are best at valuing what is bought and sold, and much of what is at stake with wetlands preservation falls off that scale— including aesthetics, social ideals and values, and biological diversity. Thus, the future of society's grappling with this issue will surely mirror its past efforts—conflict will endure, and government involvement will need to be balanced with market-oriented and voluntary efforts in an ever-vigilant manner.

Given the fact that about 75 percent of America's wetlands is in private hands, these landowners will determine how the resource is treated. The benefits of wetlands are public, but their fate rests with individuals, and solutions will require creativity and sensitivity to their interests. Should society, for example, compensate or reimburse landowners for keeping their wetlands in a natural state? Many efforts to conserve these natural resources rely on mechanisms to both encourage and compensate private landowners for good stewardship, as in use of conservation easements. Under such legal agreements, property owners voluntarily restrict specified development rights on their land through a conservation easement that is held by a government agency or qualified conservation organization. The restrictions are permanent and protect the property regardless of who owns the land in the future, yet landowners are often allowed continued use of their property for activities like agriculture, forestry, hunting, and fishing. In exchange for restricting development, landowners usually receive significant tax savings.

The Department of Agriculture offers another example through its Conservation Reserve Program and Wetlands Reserve Program, which fund the preservation and restoration of natural habitat on farmland. In the Southeast, these programs direct a large percentage of their resources toward the conservation of bottomland hardwoods, primarily through payments to farmers to allow their low-lying acreage to revert to forested wetlands. By the turn of the 21st century, some 300 square miles of cropland had been retired for this purpose, with landowners receiving about $45 per acre in "rental cost." Much of this converted cropland—especially in the lower Mississippi River valley—is reforested. The programs recognize the special advantages of allowing farms along riverbanks and agricultural lands directly in floodplains, often protected by government-built levees and drained by flood-control districts, to return to wetlands: the runoff from adjacent farm fields can be naturally absorbed and processed by the reintroduced swamps and marshes instead of flowing directly into the river. The benefits to society include reducing flood damage, creating recreational opportunities, and improving water quality.

The importance of wetlands to the United States and the world at large will only increase over time. Threats to that critical natural resource will also intensify. Understanding the history of society's attitudes and actions to these irreplaceable landscapes may not resolve the challenges facing society, but it is essential for assisting in that effort and helping to avoid the pitfalls of the past.

ACKNOWLEDGMENTS

For their generous help at various stages in this project, I would like to thank William Ainslie, Steven Anderson, Sally Atwater, Daniel Cornford, Chris Cottrill, Mitchell Dubensky, Bob Emory, Paul Forman, Joseph Hughes, Joseph Jones, Michele Justice, Kevin Kilcullen, Marcel LaFollette, Russ Lea, Thomas Lovejoy, Mark Madison, Betsy Mendelsohn, Cheryl Oakes, James O'Donnell, Donald Pisani, Leslie Overstreet, Martin Reuss, James Roan, James Shepard, Terry Sharrer, Pete Steen, Ann Vileisis, and Dennis Whigham.

SUGGESTED READING

Ainslie, William B. 2002. Forest Wetlands. In David N. Wear and John G. Greis (eds.), *Southern Forest Resource Assessment*. General Technical Report SRS-53. Asheville, NC: USDA Forest Service, Southern Research Station, 479–99.

Council for Agricultural Science and Technology. 1994. *Wetland Policy Issues*. Ames, IA: Council for Agricultural Science and Technology.

Cowardin, Lewis M., Virginia Carter, Francis C. Golet, and Edward T. LaRoe. 1979. *Classification of Wetlands and Deepwater Habitats of the United States*. Washington: GPO.

Dahl, Thomas E. 2000. *Status and Trends of Wetlands in the Conterminous United States, 1986 to 1997*. Washington: U.S. Department of the Interior, Fish and Wildlife Service.

———. 2006. *Status and Trends of Wetlands in the Conterminous United States, 1998 to 2004*. Washington: U.S. Department of the Interior, Fish and Wildlife Service.

Dahl, Thomas E., and Craig E. Johnson. 1991. *Wetlands: Status and Trends in the Conterminous United States, Mid-1970s to Mid-1980s*. Washington: GPO.

Dennis, John V. 1988. *The Great Cypress Swamps*. Baton Rouge: Louisiana State University Press.

Dennison, Mark S., and James F. Berry (eds.). 1993. *Wetlands: Guide to Science, Law, and Technology*. Park Ridge, NJ: Noyes Publications.

Dugan, Patrick (ed.). 1993. *Wetlands in Danger: A World Conservation Atlas*. New York: Oxford University Press.

Ewel, Katherine Carter, and Howard T. Odum (eds.). 1984. *Cypress Swamps*. Gainesville: University Presses of Florida.

Fredrickson, Leigh H., Sammy L. King, and Richard M. Kaminski (eds.). 2005. *Ecology and Management of Bottomland Hardwood Systems: The State of Our Understanding*. Gaylord Memorial Laboratory Special Publication No. 10. Puxico, MO: University of Missouri-Columbia.

Gallagher, Tim. 2005. *The Grail Bird: Hot on the Trail of the Ivory-billed Woodpecker*. Boston: Houghton Mifflin.

Giblett, Rodney James. 1996. *Postmodern Wetlands: Culture, History, Ecology*. Edinburgh: Edinburgh University Press.

Grunwald, Michael. 2006. *The Swamp: The Everglades, Florida, and the Politics of Paradise*. New York: Simon & Schuster.

Hays, Samuel P. 1987. *Beauty, Health, and Permanence: Environmental Politics in the United States, 1955–1985*. New York: Cambridge University Press.

Hoose, Phillip. 2004. *The Race to Save the Lord God Bird*. New York: Farrar, Straus and Giroux.

Jackson, Jerome A. 2004. *In Search of the Ivory-billed Woodpecker*. Washington: Smithsonian Books.

Journal of Forestry. 1993. Special issue on forested wetlands: 91(5) (May).

Langston, Nancy. 2003. *Where Land and Water Meet: A Western Landscape Transformed*. Seattle: University of Washington Press.

Lewis, William M., Jr. 2001. *Wetlands Explained: Wetland Science, Policy, and Politics in America*. New York: Oxford University Press.

Messina, Michael G., and William H. Conner (eds.). 1998. *Southern Forested Wetlands: Ecology and Management*. Boca Raton, FL: Lewis Publishers.

Miller, David C. 1989. *Dark Eden: The Swamp in Nineteenth-Century American Culture*. New York: Cambridge University Press.

Mitsch, William J., and James G. Gosselink. 2007. *Wetlands*, fourth edition. Hoboken, NJ: John Wiley & Sons.

National Research Council, Committee on Characterization of Wetlands. 1995. *Wetlands: Characteristics and Boundaries*. Washington: National Academy Press.

National Wetlands Newsletter. 1978–. Washington: Environmental Law Institute.

National Wetlands Working Group, Canada Committee on Ecological Land Classification. 1988. *Wetlands of Canada*. Ottawa, Ontario: Polyscience Publications.

Nelson, Megan Kate. 2005. *Trembling Earth: A Cultural History of the Okefenokee Swamp*. Athens: University of Georgia Press.

Niering, William A. 1991. *Wetlands of North America*. Charlottesville, VA: Thomasson-Grant.

Office of Technology Assessment. 1984. *Wetlands: Their Use and Regulation*. Washington: GPO.

Prince, Hugh. 1997. *Wetlands of the American Midwest: A Historical Geography of Changing Attitudes*. Chicago: University of Chicago Press.

Ripple, Jeff. 1996. *Southwest Florida's Wetland Wilderness: Big Cypress Swamp and the Ten Thousand Islands*. Gainesville: University Press of Florida.

Saikku, Mikko. 2005. *This Delta, This Land: An Environmental History of the Yazoo-Mississippi Floodplain*. Athens: University of Georgia Press.

Shaw, Samuel P., and C. Gordon Fredine. 1956. *Wetlands of the United States: Their Extent and Their Value to Waterfowl and Other Wildlife*. U.S. Fish and Wildlife Service Circular 39. Washington: GPO.

Siry, Joseph V. 1984. *Marshes of the Ocean Shore: Development of an Ecological Ethic*. College Station: Texas A&M University Press.

Stanturf, John A., and Michael G. Messina (eds.). 1997. Harvesting Impacts on Bottomland Hardwood Ecosystems. Special issue of *Forest Ecology and Management* 90(2–3) (February): 93–252.

Streever, Bill. 2001. *Saving Louisiana? The Battle for Coastal Wetlands*. Jackson: University Press of Mississippi.

Thomas, Bill. 1976. *The Swamp*. New York: W.W. Norton.

Thompson, John. 2002. *Wetlands Drainage, River Modification, and Sectoral Conflict in the Lower Illinois Valley, 1890–1930*. Carbondale: Southern Illinois University Press.

Tiner, Ralph W. 2005. *In Search of Swampland: A Wetland Sourcebook and Field Guide*, second edition. New Brunswick, NJ: Rutgers University Press.

———. 1984. *Wetlands of the United States: Current Status and Recent Trends*. Washington: GPO.

Trettin, Carl C., Martin F. Jurgensen, David F. Grigal, Margaret R. Gale, and John K. Jeglum (eds.). 1997. *Northern Forested Wetlands: Ecology and Management*. Boca Raton, FL: Lewis Publishers.

Vileisis, Ann. 1997. *Discovering the Unknown Landscape: A History of America's Wetlands*. Washington: Island Press.

Webb, Robert H., Stanley A. Leake, and Raymond M. Turner. 2007. *The Ribbon of Green: Change in Riparian Vegetation in the Southwestern United States*. Tucson: University of Arizona Press.

Whitney, Gordon G. 1994. *From Coastal Wilderness to Fruited Plain: A History of Environmental Change in Temperate North America, 1500 to the Present*. New York: Cambridge University Press.

Williams, Michael (ed.). 1990. *Wetlands: A Threatened Landscape*. Oxford, UK: Basil Blackwell.

Wilson, Anthony. 2006. *Shadow and Shelter: The Swamp in Southern Culture*. Jackson: University Press of Mississippi.

Zinn, Jeffrey A., and Claudia Copeland. 2006. *Wetland Issues*. Congressional Research Service Report IB97014. Washington: Congressional Research Service, Library of Congress.

ABOUT THE AUTHOR

Jeffrey K. Stine is Curator for Environmental History and Chair of the Division of Medicine and Science at the Smithsonian Institution's National Museum of American History. He earned his B.A., M.A., and Ph.D. in history from the University of California at Santa Barbara. Prior to joining the Smithsonian in 1989, he served as an American Historical Association Congressional Fellow with the House Committee on Science and Technology, where he assisted the special Task Force on Science Policy by writing *A History of Science Policy in the United States, 1940–1985* (1986). As an independent consultant, he has written policy histories for the U.S. Army Corps of Engineers' Office of History, the National Science Foundation's Office of Policy Research and Analysis, the American Association for the Advancement of Science's Directorate for Science and Policy Programs, the Library of Congress's Office of Scholarly Programs, and the Carnegie Commission on Science, Technology, and Government. He founded and coedited the University of Akron Press book series *Technology and the Environment* (1993–2001) and has been an editorial adviser to RFF Press since 2003. He has served as president of the American Society for Environmental History (1999–2001) and the Public Works Historical Society (2002–2003).

Stine's article "Regulating Wetlands in the 1970s: U.S. Army Corps of Engineers and the Environmental Organizations" received the Forest History Society's Frederick K. Weyerhaeuser Award for the best article published in the *Journal of Forest History* in 1983. He has been awarded several other prizes for his scholarship, including the 1992 James Madison Prize from the Society for History in the Federal Government, the 1993 G. Wesley Johnson Prize from the National Council on Public History, the 1994 Abel Wolman Award from the Public Works Historical Society, the 1995 *Choice* Outstanding Academic Book Award, and the 1999 Charles Thompson Prize from the Society for History in the Federal Government.

His publications include *Technology and Choice* (coedited with Marcel C. LaFollette; 1991), *Mixing the Waters: Environment, Politics, and the Building of the Tennessee-Tombigbee Waterway* (1993), *Twenty Years of Science in the Public Interest: A History of the Congressional Science and Engineering Fellowship Program* (1994), and *Going Underground: Tunneling Past, Present, and Future* (coedited with Howard Rosen; 1998).